TRIAL BY SASSWOOD

MARKET DAY

TRIAL BY
SASSWOOD

by
Esther Warner

with
sketches by
JOSS

London 1956

READERS UNION · VICTOR GOLLANCZ

For Sadie Rogers
who knew that the only difference in colour which matters
is the dye of a person's thoughts
and for Oakley Parker
who was never known to look down on any man, neither up
but always level, as becomes a friend

This RU edition was produced in 1956
for sale to its members only by Readers Union Ltd 38 William IV
Street, Charing Cross, London, W.C.2, from whom full particulars
may be obtained. This edition has been newly set in 11 on 12 pt
Bembo type, printed and bound by C. Tinling & Co. Ltd, Prescot,
Lancashire. The book was first published by Victor Gollancz Ltd in 1955.

CONTENTS

A*

FOREWORD

WHEN PEOPLE who know that I have lived in Africa ask me about the causes of the recent (though they are not recent) troubles there, they usually seem to expect big round answers couched in terms of economics or sociology or political science. I do not know any big round answers, nor even the vocabulary of the specialists.

Droves of professional investigators have fanned out over the globe recently, travelling widely to discover sensible answers to knotty problems. We have sent them in our panic to survive, and in our desire to be understood and appreciated. They have told us what they have found in a number of excellent recent books. Our problems have to be seen in the round, and if some of the experts have seemed to generalize too much about *peoples,* it is because matters are too urgent for them to take time to know *persons,* except as best they can in hasty interviews.

This story is one of persons whose lives became part of my own. It is my answer (fragmentary, I know), but it is not my book. It is Comma's and Johnny's and Bola's and their kinsmen's. It is not imperative, except as friendship and understanding, no matter on how small a scale, have become imperative. It is not scholarly, except that the kind of wisdom Emerson and Thoreau gave us can be heard in the folk-lore of the deep forests of Africa. It is not assertive, for friendship needs no vindication, and is its own compulsion.

ESTHER S. WARNER

Costa Mesa,
California

I

BLOOD-RAIN

*A blackened name will not weather
itself bright. The smudge will fall away only
when scoured by the hand that fouled it.*

IF THE first storm of the long Liberian rainy season spills its
fury over the land just before dark when the sun is flaming
fiercely between banks of swirling indigo clouds, the drops
when they fall seem tinged with red. Blood-rain, the tribes-
people call this, and it is known to be evil.

I stood at the bar of the plantation clubhouse looking out
of the open window-wall over the top of distant jungle as
the murky clouds piled up in the sky. They rolled and churned
like huge slate-coloured barrels wallowing through heavy seas.

A few yards beyond the club where the parking lot ends on
the verge of a precipice, a lanky boy sat in the back of a red
pick-up, a drum cradled between his knees. His body was
tensed around the wooden cylinder as though it were the core
of his being. He flicked the sides of his long hands against the
drum head, making it speak in choppy thrums.

'Comma is making the drum cry for him.' Johnny, my
steward boy, was back of the bar glugging Coca-Cola syrup
out of a gallon jug. He jerked his head in the direction of the
pick-up.

Comma struck the drum near the outer edges. There was
no lift or lilt in it. The pauses in rhythm were like gasps for
breath between sobs. Some three months previous, I had seen
him pound the centre of that drum with the palms of his hands,

pummelling it so hard that it had seemed the force that lifted the heels of the houseboys dancing over the dew-studded lawn. His head had been thrown back and high that night. The other boys were prancing for his good fortune in being sent on a responsible errand.

We had entrusted him with fifty dollars, more than any of them earned in a year. After he had trekked to his home village and had rested a few days with his people, he was to bring back the chimpanzee he planned to purchase with the money (we were collecting the animals for export to a breeding farm in Florida). Instead of appearing at the end of three weeks, he had been gone three months. When he did show up, he had neither animal nor money, his clothes were hanging askew in dirty tatters, and he had been beaten until his swollen features were scarcely recognizable.

I did not care about the lost money; I was too contrite over my thoughtlessness in sending him unguarded through the forests with that sum, more than most natives are able to amass intact during a lifetime of labour. What *did* matter was that Comma's plans for his future had been wrecked. He was mission-schooled, a promising student who had won a scholarship for medical training down the coast. No one believed the story he told about being robbed, not of the money, but of the chimpanzee. There were gaps and contradictions in his tale which he told in trailing sentences and with shifty eyes. When asked why he had been gone twelve weeks instead of three, he stammered that he had lost track of time, it was as though he had been out of the world. Yet his wounds were obviously new, recently inflicted.

Sticky Cola overflowed Johnny's glass and ran unheeded along the polished mahogany while we stood there listening, seeing Comma's back bent like a pulled bow, taut with grief, against the darkening forest and the gathering storm. The trickling syrup ran over the edge of the bar, splotched the skirt of my white evening dress with ruddy streaks, puddled between the straps of my silver slippers. Johnny righted the jug with maddening slowness and ran his forefinger through the pool on the counter. The Cola was about the colour of his own skin. Then he wrapped his amazingly long and red tongue around his sweetened finger while he coldly regarded the stain on my dress.

'Poor Boy can wash it out tomorrow,' he said with weary indifference. 'But Poor Boy cannot wash the stain off Comma's spoiled name! Nor can any person, only you, Missy, *who don't want to!*'

Johnny had a deep voice and he put drum-boom into the end of his sentence, the big drum, the one they call simply, 'the man'. It was evidence of his hostility that he had called me 'Missy'. That is the accepted way for a servant on the plantation to address his employer's wife, but it had seldom been used at my house since Comma had come to us. He had called me 'Mommio' from the beginning and the others had taken it up. Any honoured native woman is called 'Ma', of which 'Mommio' is the diminutive and affectionate form. When my servants used it the difference in our skins was minimized. By calling me 'Missy' Johnny was reminding me that I was white and had done a typically 'white thing' when I had sent Comma to the interior. Doing the white thing by someone implies in Liberia, not a vicious or deliberately brutal act, but a thoughtless one which often has brutal consequences.

Comma had said, and the other boys had backed him up, that if I would walk to his village, I would learn the truth about what had happened, and that I would be able to clear him with the Mission. They had only hinted at first that this was the least I could do to right matters. When the hints did not seem to register, they had reasoned, pleaded, and finally turned hostile, saying that I didn't care whether I polished clean the name that I had helped to blacken.

Johnny's feelings were evident in his behaviour toward me. Had he been in his usual mommio-mood, he would have by this time been on my side of the counter, dabbing frantically at my stained skirt with a damp towel. Instead, he continued to scoop Cola out of the dark puddle and lick it with his tongue while his big eyes indicted me for whiteness. Comma's drum throbbed sorrowfully on and on. Nothing seemed to change except the light. When I first noticed Comma wrapped around his drum, the sky behind him flamed a fierce red through breaks in banks of swirling indigo clouds. The departing sun seemed to have burned holes through them, reddening all the landscape. The first big drops if they fell before dark would be blood-rain, and would bring bad luck. Far better for the first rain to burst in the night!

In an adjoining room, the club juke-box had broken down as was its intermittent custom, and a group of white planters were delivering experimental kicks and curses at the cabinet in an abortive effort to jar the mechanism back into action. The kicks seemed the counterpoise of Comma's drum – white men kicking out their frustration against the veneer sides of a monstrously ugly and lighted musical machine while Comma felt his out through his hands as they fluttered over the edges of a home-crafted hollow log.

'If you had not made big-mouth about Comma's trip, it would never have reached the ears of the mission people. Do you know that, Johnny?'

I was doing the accusing now. Ever since Comma's return, I had been on the defensive. The white people shrugged and said, 'Well, what did you expect? You should have known better.' The blacks acted as though the whole thing had been a plot on my part to ruin Comma's reputation. In their eyes, the fact that I did not want to walk to the interior to investigate Comma's story proved that I did not care what became of him.

'Humph!' Johnny shrugged off all responsibility. 'When fifty dollars runs away, it makes a rumble louder than an elephant's belly. Everyone hears it for his own self.'

'The truth makes a strong sound also,' I said. 'Why doesn't Comma sinply tell the truth?'

'Red is not a bright colour in the dark,' Johnny said cryptically. 'In Lomaland, you would see light.'

Events are thought by tribal Africans to have a life-force of their own, *a will to get done*. The time of break-through, the moment when human resistance is most vulnerable, is just before the first storm. The shades of departed Old Ones, their spirits housed in stick figures carved in blackened wood, are then charged with special potency. As the skies become increasingly sinister, it is a time of apprehension and prayer all through the forests. The spirits, who know what things are trying to get done, are asked to indicate which ones should be helped, which hindered. Johnny knew that if 'a trip to Lomaland was trying to get the white woman to walk it', this brooding hour was the most favourable time to make me feel the compulsion of the journey.

I had walked across Liberia twice, joyously, and I suppose I would have been willing to do it again, grudgingly perhaps this time, if I had thought that any good might come of it. But leave time was at hand, I was dull from sun and malaria, and I was not willing to trek for a week on the vague promise that I would 'see light'.

'I can't do it, Johnny. If I tripped on a creeper, there would not be strength in me to get up again.'

'I will lift you up, and put your feet back under you, Mommio. I am going with you!'

He spoke of the journey as though it were decided upon. During the past two years, he had often known and sometimes voiced what I was going to do before I had known myself that I had made a decision. This was not clairvoyance, I think, but had come from a thorough knowledge of me which had grown through all the small exchanges of daily household doings.

'You!' I scoffed. 'You said on the last trip that if you lived to get back to the plantation, you would never set foot to the path again. Now you want to walk to Sierra Leone.'

'I like to talk a big trip,' Johnny admitted. 'I have talked that other trip until it is worn down thin. But, ah! This one! Enough talk will come out of it to last me until I am an old man with no teeth. Besides, those other trips were just to see what we could see. This one is to save Comma.'

'The paths will run like rivers,' I argued. 'All the little wading creeks will be big swims. How will we manage when our feet can't find the bottom and the big old tree trunks thick as a house are coming down on us?'

Even the tribes-people keep to their huts during the worst of the deluge, 'to keep our *hearts warm,*' they say, 'even if the skin did not get wet in the weather.' I have seen the women creeping out timidly to bring in jars of water which must settle before it is clear enough to drink, seen them shudder at the force and swiftness of the rivers which flow past their villages. A house-roof rushes past, tossed on the flood-crest as though it were a fallen leaf. A dead goat swirls by, its white upper side scarcely stained by the mud-red water. A canoe bobs along, empty.

Old mothers have told me that during the storm season, a woman must receive her man gently at night and comfort him as she would comfort fearful children. 'In the rain time, a man's hunger for his woman begins in his heart and makes a slow journey to his belly. In other seasons, his hunger makes no journey. It lives in his belly the whole time.' This is the folk-saying they have made to give their daughters storm-knowledge.

Johnny knew all this, knew more about the moods and fury of tropical storms than I, yet he was willing to expose himself to the elements for the sake of helping clear Comma's 'spoiled name'. Johnny had a low opinion of literacy and could not understand why Comma wanted to go on to school, but, like every other tribesman, he knew the value of a good reputation and that a blackened name does not weather itself bright.

'Oh,' he said lightly, 'when we come to the deep rivers, I will just make myself into a big old black barracuda, and swim over with you on my back, my Mommio.'

He was as happy now as though the trip were decided upon (as I suppose it was). He whooshed a towel over the counter with his sprightliest steward's flourish. For some unaccountable reason, the machine in the next room had begun to function. *At Last,* again. *At last my lonely days are over. . . .* Comma's hollow log had lost to the machine.

There was a rush to the bar then, as though to celebrate this small victory. Actually, it was the gathering storm which herded us together. We were loudly scornful of the way tapping boys on the rubber plantation insist on sleeping ganged up during the storm season, fifteen or twenty to a single small hut while other houses stand empty. They sleep in heaps on the floor, a tangle of crossed legs and arms and bodies, and some of them lie on the rafters with legs and arms entwined around roof-poles. But here we were crushed together in a room too small for the half of us, feeling that same need to be many persons, close together, massed against the fury gathering outside.

For white men, the storms are worse in some ways than for the Africans. In a time when all that is loose is lost, they know that no heart-ties moor them to this alien land. *At last my lonely days are over. . . .* The song lied and we knew it. Our lonely days were not over.

A stab of lightning crackled across the sky, seeming to slit the heavy clouds wide open, like a spear ripping through paper bags. Wind drove the water horizontally above the earth. Half the floor was drenched before we could batten the doors. It had come, finally; after the heat, after the tense dusty waiting, the rains had come. The phonograph scratched on, the words blurred by wind and water.

The storm drove Comma inside. He was behind the bar with Johnny and another houseboy, Philo. All of them were mixing drinks at top speed, reaching for the empty extended glass, remembering by some peculiar magic what had been in it last, handing it back filled, reaching for another, and another.

What happened next was a blur of shouts and fists. A can opener was the immediate cause, but anything else would have served as well.

The can opener was an innovation supplied by the planter who had charge of the clubhouse that month, a man whom the houseboys called 'Ants', this being short for 'ants-between-the-buttocks', because he habitually jumped around as though a driver ant were biting him in that locality. Ants was inordinately proud of the new gadget. It made him nervous, he said, the way houseboys clip off the top of a tin with one neat swipe of a cutlass. After he had dreamed that his own head had been severed in this manner, he had imported two can openers, one for himself and one for the club. No more cutlasses!

Comma started to open a can of olives in the usual way, one well-aimed stroke of the big blade. Ants bellowed with rage, reached across the bar, and caught Comma's arm midway in the swing. The deflected edge gashed his leg. Johnny, watching the blood seep through Comma's clothing, grabbed the can and jammed it in the gadget. When the crank would not turn, he took both hands to it, and with strength born of terror, snapped the crank. The planters, who then tried to restrain Ants, found he had the strength of several and everyone had an opportunity to unbottle the angers which had pressured up with the storm, flailing blindly at anyone because anyone had swung at him.

When we were finally home, I went downstairs with bandages and aspirin for Comma. He was wadded up in a tight ball of misery on Johnny's bed.

'Let me see your cut leg,' I said.

Comma made no answer. One clenched fist was between his teeth and he was biting it.

Johnny shook his head at me. 'Comma can not loose his trousers in front of you, Mommio, he learned shame at the Mission. Never mind the cut. I will find spider-webs to put in it.'

When I laid my hand across Comma's forehead, he suddenly uncoiled and snatched at my hand with both of his, clinging to me like a small child.

'That old Ants,' Johnny grumbled. 'When you go to his house, Mommio, and the steward boy Philo asks you what to drink, I want you to order Cola.'

'Why, Johnny?'

'Well, the liquor is going to have medicine in it,' Johnny said. 'You know that stupid Philo that works there? Well, Philo has been stealing whisky from old Ants' chop cupboard. Ants saw the bottle dropped down too fast, so he began to mark the bottle. Philo saw the marks, so he just added water up to the lowest mark each time he took some out. Then, Ants saw the whisky get lighter each day, so I told Philo what he must add so the colour will not change.'

'Well?'

'Well, it wasn't vinegar I told Philo to use.' Johnny giggled. 'God put that fine idea in my head. It was to help Philo. Now Philo will steal only once from each new bottle. When I was blessed with this fine idea, I went right out in the rain and made water in the gas tank of the motor car Ants drives. Before he gets home tonight, the motor will die. He will have to walk in the rain to the closest labour camp and get plenty of boys to put strength behind him and push him all the way home. This will show him the value of strength. You heard all that he said about using your head and not your strength after I broke his foolish old can opener! So, OK, I used my head to teach him about strength.

'Now,' Johnny went on, his round little pug-face all crimped with sympathy for Comma and satisfaction in what he was going to say, 'won't that Ants be hot-mad when he hears we are going to walk all the way to Lomaland in the rain just to clear old Comma here?'

'I haven't said I was going, Johnny.'

Comma stopped groaning to listen.

'Oh, but you are going, Mommio. Maybe you don't know it yet, but you are!' Johnny nodded, solemn as a sibyl.

'What makes you so sure? I wish you would not always be trying to manage me, Johnny.'

His face blanked into wide-eyed innocence. 'Why I never managed you into it, Mommio. That trip is just like a hen-egg ready to hatch. All I did was to chip the shell a little so what is ready to come can get out more easy.'

There was the sound of a screen door banging, a 'Helooo, anybody home? Where'd everybody go?'

It was Ants, drunk and drenched. 'Car stalled. Guess you'll have to put me up for the night. How about a nightcap? Sure could use one!'

'I'll fix the drink.' Johnny bustled with alacrity. 'And I'll bring you Cola, Mommio.' His stomach was wobbling with the mirth he couldn't contain much longer.

'No, you won't,' I said firmly. 'You go dress the bed.'

'What's so damn funny?' the man asked.

'Oh,' Johnny explained, 'I was just laughing about the way we will have to open cans on the trail. We don't have a machine for it, so I guess I will just have to rip the lids off with my teeth. I have rather strong teeth. See?' He pulled back the corners of his lips with his fingers, baring an amazingly white and perfect set of over-size molars. Johnny's eyes grew milky, filmed with hate as he held the awful grimace. I saw my guest's hand tremble slightly as he reached toward his throat to unbutton his collar, as though he suddenly found it chokingly tight.

'You see,' Johnny went on when he couldn't hold his lips back any longer, 'the Mommio and I are going to walk to Lomaland to clean Comma's spoiled name. Comma is the boy you cut and kicked tonight. The blood is still running out of his leg. I go now to put spiderwebs in it.'

The man did not so much as glance at Johnny now. He tried to fix his wavering stare on me.

'That's not true, is it? You going to Lomaland?'

'Yes, it is!' I told him. 'I am going.' But I had not known until that moment that I was.

'You're on their side,' he moaned. He looked ready to weep. 'They stole your money, and they broke my nice new can opener, and you're on their side. I hope you drown!'

'We won't,' Johnny said impudently. I saw him reach under the sheet he was drawing over the guest bed and carefully bunch the mattress pad into a series of diagonal lumps.

'I have prepared your bed now, sir,' he announced cheerfully.

Now that I was committed to the trip, I experienced a feeling of relief, even anticipation. This was partly, I suppose, because I felt that the physical discomforts – the drenchings, the sluddering through mud and swamp-slime, the uncertainty of finding shelter at night – were a sort of penance I could pay for my mistake in judgment. Afterwards, I could go back to the United States knowing that even though I were unable to reverse the incidents which had put a blight on Comma's future, I had made an effort. I knew that it was partly for myself that I wanted to go. When you have been part of the reason that another person cannot hold his head high, you have got to walk it off. Black-white friction in Africa is an albatross-weight which is less burdensome if one wears it willingly around the neck than if he tries to pitch it from him.

I had some misgivings about the wisdom of further schooling for Comma, but I had to admit his right to attempt it.

I was sure that he already knew a great many more facts than he understood. He was like the boys of the Mandingo tribes who learn to write phrases from the Koran on little wooden slates, but have no idea what they are writing, only that it is 'good'.

A stillicide of steady rain hung a curtain of lulling sound around the house. I slept, deeply rested. It was not the song of the pepper bird, that feathered alarm-clock of West Africa, which roused me, but the din of many voices under the house. Louder than any of the others was Johnny's.

'Shut up, you people,' he was bellowing. 'Tie your mouths! You will wake the Mommio. She needs strength for the path.' They subsided into murmurings. 'All right! Now keep your tongues down and I will tell you how it was at the club last night.'

'*Ha-o!* [Right!]' They were roaring with delight. The loudest of them seemed directly under my bed.

'Now this' (Johnny was indicating some object I supposed) 'is the music machine. Now you, Dika, and you Latoka, are going to be planter mens. You are going to kick the machine to make it work. See? Now I am going to be me, Johnny. You tell me, Latoka, how strength is of no use. Tell me that only big thinks in the head are of any worth. Tell me how all white men have everything because their heads are full of big thinks! But if your head is black, there is no room in it for even little thinks. You break everything because all you have got is strength which is of no use. Go on, Latoka, tell me. Tell me all that and then *kick* the music box to make it work. Then all of you kick it. Kick it until the sides break!' His rising voice shrilled with bitterness.

Latoka said this and a lot more in which he did not need to be coached. '*Ha-o! Ha-o!*' The crowd roared above the hollow sound of metal crumpling.

Before Johnny could give stage directions for the second act, I stopped the play by rapping on the floor.

'You stupid people,' Johnny yelled at them. 'You woke the Mommio. I told you to tie your big mouths. I better go fetch her some coffee to cool her vex. Go now! *Mu!*'

Johnny did not say anything but a sheepish 'Moin [Good morning]' until I had had most of the coffee.

'Who are all those people under the house? How can you let them spoil my sleep?' The coffee had not cooled all of my vex.

'Those noisy people under the house want to be carriers,' Johnny explained sheepishly. 'They want me to speak for them, how their necks are as wide as their jaws from the head-loads they have already carried. That big old Zabogi wants to be headman. It is most necessary for Zabogi to go to his home in Lomaland. He must take his wife there.'

'Why? Is Tama going to have another baby?' Since Tama insisted on bearing her children in her own village, her frequent pregnancies had been a considerable inconvenience to Zabogi's employer, who had regularly to get along without the useful Zabogi.

'No *pickin* this time,' Johnny laughed. 'Zabogi has got to take Tama home to beat her.'

'Why can't he beat her here on the plantation, if he has got to beat her?'

Johnny looked his amazement. 'You are not awake yet, Mommio, or you would not ask that one. You must know that the good of beating is not in the hurt of the whip but in the shame of it. It is no use to beat Tama if she is not shamed before her own people.'

'What did Tama do that she must walk seven days to get a beating?'

'She did a plenty bad thing! *Tama has been frisky!* If Zabogi does not beat her good, no one, not even Tama, will respect him again. You know that Zabogi is a big man in his village. Some day he will be chief. How can he chief a village if he

cannot even chief a woman? *Zabogi loves Tama!* So, he will
take the trouble to walk to Lomaland to beat her.'

'I do not want Tama along,' I said.

'Tama will walk as a man.' Johnny was pleading for
her.

'You mean Tama will not sleep with Zabogi on the trail?
That would only make it worse when she is already in trouble
for man-palaver.'

'I mean she will not ask for all the take-care you get on the
trail because you are a woman.' His expression changed the
contour of his face as though the thought were ageing him
while I watched. I knew he wanted to say, 'Let us not speak
of this thing which neither of us can help.'

Although I had never travelled in a hammock under a
frame resting on men's heads except once when I was ill, it
was true that I had been pampered on my jungle trips. I had
been carried 'piggy-back' through swamp ooze and clay muck.
I had crossed swift streams sitting on a swimming man's
shoulders. The creepers had been hacked from paths in front
of me. I had been pulled by the hand up steep inclines by
men who had sixty-pound loads on their heads. Being a
woman, I had accepted these aids as a woman, not as a white.
Thinking now of the complexities of having Tama along, I
recognized the convenient deceit I had perpetuated and come
to believe.

'You mean, don't you Johnny, that Tama will not expect
to be taken care of like a white woman?' It seemed better to
get our thoughts out in the open.

'Yes, Mommio,' he said, softly, sadly, 'that is what I was
trying to say.' Neither of us spoke for a while. It was he who
rallied first.

'Oh well,' he said, 'never mind. No one can help the kind
of skin he got borned into. Let me tell you something,
Mommio. Maybe you don't know this but the first mens in
the world got made out of clay. God had such a hellova fine

time making them that he made too many. They wouldn't all go in God's kiln. The baked ones came out black and strong and made to last. The others just got put on a mat and laid around, left over, in God's compound. They are sun-baked and white like the clay they were made from. They break easy. That is why the strong black ones have to take care of the easy-break white ones. Now, we like to take care of you. It is no fault of yours that you did not get baked proper. What we don't like is when people like that old Ants says our strength is of no use. *We have got strength because God picked us up first!*'

Ants! I remembered then that he had slept in the house. Surely he was not still asleep after all the commotion.

'Where is he, Johnny? Does he keep to his bed?'

'Oh, no,' Johnny said, 'he caught a ride to the Trading Company to get another car to drive. What do you think he did before he left? He asked for Comma, and when I had fetched Comma, Ants gave him a shilling – said it would heal the cut in Comma's leg. *White people sure think there is a heellova medicine in money!*'

'And Comma? How is he? Is he able to walk the trail?'

'Comma would go to Lomaland if he had to walk on his knees,' Johnny said, 'for when you see that his name is clean, you will tell the people at the Mission and they will let him go to the grand school. They will believe you, because you are white.'

I should not have tried to dodge that. 'They will believe me because they have known me a long time,' I said.

'They have know Comma longer,' Johnny pointed out. 'They have know him ever since he was a small boy and they took him in. No, it is because you are white that they will believe you. When a white person says something, all the other white people believe it until it is proved a lie. When a black person says something, all the white people think it is a lie unless the black one can somehow prove it is truth!

Mommio, let me ask you something. What is the colour of your tongue?'

'It is red,' I said, 'just like yours!'

'That's just it,' he said. 'Words come out of the inside of a person. Inside, we are all the same colour. What has the colour on the outside of a person got to do with the colour of his thinks? Does the skin dye the words after they leave the tongue?'

'Johnny,' I said, 'the only difference between people's colour that is of any importance is the dye of their thoughts.'

'Hellova true!' he agreed. 'If white people were one part as smart as they think they are, they would all know that.'

'Many do know it. Every day you tell me how bad white people are. Sometimes you should give me your ear [listen to me] when I tell you about some good ones. Not all white people are bad; not all black people are good.'

'White people can write,' he said, as though that explained something.

'Comma can write, and he is not white. The Chinese, who have yellow skins, made the first books.'

Johnny was not interested in the Chinese. 'It is of no use for Comma to know how to write,' he said. 'Who will believe the dye-talk of a black man? But you are white, so people will believe the dye-talk you make. That is why I tell you about the bads of the white. That is why I want you to see that when a black man speaks what is true hot oil that rolls in a boil will not burn his hand, a hot cutlass will not mark his back, and no bad can reach him in any part!' Johnny was referring to Comma's plan: he wanted to stand trial by ordeal in his home village in my presence. In his mind and in the minds of the Africans, this would completely clean his 'spoiled name'. What I could not make him nor any of the other houseboys understand was that such a trial would carry no weight with the missionaries, who were the only ones who needed to be convinced of his honesty Not only would they entirely reject the verdict of such a trial, they would be disappointed in me for permitting it The whole thing would only deepen their mistrust of Comma unless I could discover some incidental intelligence which would exonerate him. During the drama of the trial everyone in the town would be thinking about the events which had led up to it. It was my hope that during this group concentration on these incidents some chance remark would furnish a clue that I could follow up. Johnny did not know much more Loma than I, so any English I would overhear would have to come from Zabogi, or Tama, or some of the carriers, or Comma himself. Africans know that 'sasswood' (trial by ordeal) is infallible The guilty perish and the innocent are unscathed None of them could believe that white people are either too stupid, or have too feeble a belief in the power of virtue, to credit a trial by ordeal. Comma's insistence on being tried in this manner was enough to convince any of them that he was innocent.

'Go ask Comma to tell you the story about Shadrach and the fiery-furnace,' I suggested. 'He can read it to you.'

'Tonight,' Johnny said. 'Stories taste better at night. And now I have things to make ready for the path. What shall I tell Zabogi, Mommio? Does Tama walk with us?' He seemed a little too eager to settle this point. It was not like him to go to that much trouble for someone not of his own Bassau tribe, unless the issue involved black against white.

I liked Tama. She had taught me to weave circular rice-bags of raffia, saying my hands had sense in them, scolding my 'stupid feet' when the strands tied to my toes became a hopeless tangle. Tama and I had laughed at many things. Now that her 'walking like a man' was decided, I really believed I would like to have her along.

'If Tama has got all the frisky out of her, we will take her,' I decided. 'But first, I want to see her and make some strong woman-talk to her. Why are *you* speaking for Tama, Johnny?'

'Oh, Mommio,' he laughed, 'how can you think the thing

that is in your head now? I don't need a frisky woman. I need
Zabogi. If he is our headman, there will be no palaver on the
path. All Loma men respect him. If a carrier set down his load
and ran away, that man could never again go to Lomaland if
Zabogi is our bossman. Also, Zabogi can name the carriers.
I would fear the strong medicine [voodoo] of the ones I left
out if I had to call their names.'

'All right, send word to Zabogi. And now, another matter.
How is Poor Boy to make our clothes clean for the trip?
Can a broken music-machine hold wash water?'

'Mommio,' he said, 'you have got eyes that can see through
the floor, for true. I will tell you how we will manage. Ants
will buy us a new tub. Comma does not want that shilling
he got to heal his leg. He says there is bad luck in it. He spits
on it. We will use the money to buy the new tub.'

Johnny opened the curtains. 'The day is fine,' he said. 'The
rainy season will not be so bad this time. No blood-rain fell
in the first storm. See? The sun is making the paths dry for
us. Up, Mommio! Make we ready, make we go!'

II

SAWDUST AND SAND

*Money is no use to a man until he spends it
for something that is.*

A CURMUDGEON of a chimpanzee was responsible in the
beginning for my getting involved in Comma's destiny.
The chimpanzees we collected were eventually sent to
an animal-breeding farm in Florida, but while they lived with
us they were, as Johnny said, getting the bush out of their
hair and growing some manners. Town Chief was the only
one of them who ever had to be caged or chained. He was
a surly tyrant and a wino.

I was working under the house wedging some pottery clay
the morning Town Chief went berserk and Comma arrived
on the scene. Things were tranquil enough in the beginning.
Poor Boy sat before a galvanized tub of foaming suds washing
our clothes in the usual way, a bar of soap in his left hand
with a scrap of muslin stretched over it. With his right hand
he rubbed the soiled spots on each garment over the soap
cake. Beside him, hovered over a smaller tub of suds, were
several chimpanzees imitating him exactly as they scrubbed
some cleaning rags. This was a substitution device to keep
them from lending him doubtful assistance in his own tub.
Sammi, the cook, was beating palm kernels in a mortar. His
beautiful wife sat with her back against a house pillar, weaving
bamboo fish-traps. In the living-room above us, Johnny was
dancing over the floor, a blanket tied to each foot, to glaze
the wax into mirror finish. We were all working to the

rhythm of a little under-arm drum which Buno thumped daily for the floor-polishing dance. We sang a catchy Bassau work-song over and over with innovations supplied first by one and then another. Everyone was busy and happy except Town Chief, who glowered at all he could see of the world from the door of his little bamboo hut a few feet away.

Town Chief never learned how to take part in group activity, animal or human. A chain from his collar dangled over his fat stomach and was attached to a post in the earth. He beat his paunch rhythmically with the chain; otherwise he just sat there leering at us. Now and then he would pull back his thin lips to bare an impressive set of teeth. Lali, the little female chimp to whom he was emotionally attached even though she had not reached a nubile age, would look up uneasily from the wash tub at intervals as though she expected her lord and master to call her home for a good beating and to explain why she had dared enjoy herself away from him. I knew from past experiences with Town Chief that the chain-flopping was a nervous mannerism but that his soundless tooth-baring was a forecast that his bad disposition or bad digestion was about to overcome any restraint he might be showing at the moment.

To give him an activity like the rest of us, I found some palm nuts for him to crack and supplied him with two rocks, one to lay the kernels on while he cracked them open with the other. He was really professional about this and would allow Lali to sit wistfully beside him picking up the crumbs while he devoured the plump whole kernels, pausing some-times to indicate his complete satisfaction with alarming digestive noises. If any of the monkeys or the other chim-panzees came within range while he was thus engaged, he would bite or strike them. Lali could not wear a bright bangle around her neck as all the chimpanzees liked to do, because if the food was finished before his hunger, he would twist the necklace until it choked her, as though the fault were hers.

When I gave him the bunch of palm kernels he let out a roar, a command to Lali to hurry to his side and watch him stuff himself.

After Sammi had finished with the mortar he went across the yard to a neighbour's house to borrow a cup of palm wine. We used this to leaven bread because of the wild yeast it accumulated. Our own stock was exhausted; we had killed six chickens the night before and Sammi had insisted as usual that the meat would be tough enough to break our teeth if the fowls did not spend their last moments completely relaxed.

Palm wine is the fermented sap of palm trees. Around any forest village (unless it is peopled by Mohammedans who do not drink intoxicants) are hundreds of tapped palm trees with gourd containers tied to the trunks to catch the flow. Chimpanzees living in the jungle have learned to rob these containers and so become addicts even though they have never lived in a village. Town Chief was drunk when he was captured. In fact, he was captured because he was drunk, adult males being extremely difficult to take when they are in possession of their normal considerable strength. Our other chimpanzees had been taken as babies, incidental booty when their mothers to whom they were clinging were killed for food. Although Town Chief was impossible to handle when he was sober, he became docile under the influence. Animal Boy had learned that the only way to clean Chief's hut was to bring on the palm wine. After several avid gulps of a pint or so each, Chief would lie down with his hands clasped under his head, his raised knees crossed, and on his face an expression of sheer bliss. Half sober, he would let a child lead him around by the hand; cold sober he was formidable.

Sammi didn't think, I suppose, of what unfulfilled desires a whiff of palm juice could arouse in Town Chief when he sauntered by with the borrowed wine in his hand. At first the chimp thought it was cage-cleaning time. He opened his enormous slit of a mouth expectantly and held out his hand

B

for the cup. When Sammi walked on past, Town Chief went wild. He screamed and lunged at Sammi until the end of the chain brought him up short with a jerk. He then hurled one of the rocks and, with surprising accuracy of aim, glanced it off Sammi's skull. Sammi shrieked. Lali yelped her terror as she ran to me and plumped herself down on my foot, hugging my knees and burrying her terrified little mug in my skirt. Town Chief then picked up the remaining rock and brought it down smartly with all the strength in his big long arm on the padlock, which was smashed. Free now, he stood in the door of his house, and like Samson in the temple, brought the structure down in a heap. Perhaps nothing more would have happened if everyone who was not already screaming had not begun to yell and run. This, naturally, gave Town Chief the idea of pursuit. He was really after Sammi's palm wine, I think. Sammi darted through the screen door of his quarters and Town Chief simply went through the screen. They emerged almost simultaneously, but Sammi soon had a slight lead. As he sprinted past his wife he handed her the cup of sloshing wine. She wheeled off at an angle as fast as a heavily pregnant woman can, but Chief caught her by the leg and she fell, outscreaming all the rest of the frenzied uproar.

Monsieur Padrone, who lived in the next house, was standing at the moment in his bathroom, clad only in a pair of striped shorts and a Santa Claus beard of shaving lather. A glance out of the window convinced him that this was no time to think of the proprieties so he joined the chase as he was, followed by all of his houseboys. Johnny and Buno were there too, the clumps of blankets still tied to their flying feet. I was considerably impeded in motion because I could not dislodge Lali from my foot. Just who was chasing whom was difficult to decide. They were all chasing Town Chief until he decided to chase one of them. Monsieur Padrone had hold of the end of the chain once, but instead of leaning away and allowing himself to be dragged, Town Chief started coming up the chain hand over hand. My neighbour wisely let loose amid a shower of loosened soap bubbles and profanity. The other chimps were in a huddle, bottoms raised, heads and arms beating the ground.

Into this bedlam walked a tall strange boy as calmly as though the situation were everyday. When his path intersected Town Chief's and the beast turned to attack him, he did not run. He just stood there calmly waiting. This surprised Town Chief enough to slow him down. The boy then held out both hands towards those terrible gnashing white teeth. I saw his lips move but in the din I could not hear what he said. Town Chief came to a full stop. Then he took one of the boy's outstretched hands as though they were old buddies and he was tired of the whole stupid show. He looked at the rest of us defiantly and then confidently at his ally. Hand in hand, the tall lithe boy and the stubby swart little animal walked slowly toward the house.

'All right!' said the boy. 'If you want to tie him to the pillar there, take the end of the chain while I make talk to him.'

They sat down side by side on the ground. The boy patted the animal on the head and spoke in low tones in the Loma language, almost whispering in his ear. The others tiptoed around the pillar, fastening the end of the chain with a rope. Lali left me then, scampering over to Chief's side, looking up at him worshipfully with her bright-bead eyes. Chief ignored her completely. The boy droned on and on finally Chief curled up in a ball and fell into an exhausted sleep with his head on the boy's lap.

'I give you my thanks,' I said then. Sitting there on the ground, he was no taller than the Bassau boys who sat too, now that Town Chief was both asleep and secured. The difference in length was in the legs, the Bassaus being squat and stocky while the Lomas are usually long-limbed and lean. 'What can I dash [give] you now that you have helped us?'

'What I wish is to stay with you,' he said. 'I wish to take care of all your animals.'

'I agree,' I said. 'I certainly agree! What was it you said to Town Chief when he came charging toward you with his teeth out in front?'

'Well,' he said, looking down with what seemed too much modesty, 'first I gave him the courtesy pause as all our people are taught to do. Then I told him my name, which is the proper thing to do when a man meets a stranger. I spoke to him in English, so he would hear his own language. That is also proper if one is able to do it. I said ,"My name is Comma. The meaning of it is to give pause." So, the chimpanzee gave pause and I took him by the hand, as you saw.'

The boy's voice was soft and rich and clear. I think of sun shining through amber when I remember the sound of Comma's voice.

'How much money will I see for the work?' Comma asked. His large dark eyes took on an extra shine when he spoke of money.

'A shilling, each day,' I said in a flush of gratitude. Perhaps any of us could have done what Comma did if he had thought of doing it. The difference was that Comma did think of it. The Bassaus, I learned later, credited Loma magic rather than intelligence for the capture.

Johnny started to speak and then changed his mind. The Bassaus were exchanging dark looks. Wages are pretty well standardized on the plantation and custom has it that cook and stewards rate top pay and privilege. Johnny earned a shilling and Sammi a few cents more. I knew as soon as had spoken that bad feeling would come from it. I was no only paying too much for the kind of work but, what was worse, I had introduced a feared Loma into an all-Bassau ménage. Within Liberia, which is about the size of Maine there are some twenty-odd tribes. In the old days, it wa unsafe for a member of one tribe to cross the boundary o another. Trade goods coming up from the coast were handed from tribe to tribe at the borders with a rise in price accompanying each successive transfer. They still tell you about the slave raids their ancestors lived through and which tribes raided others to get captives to be sold on the coast. The Firestone Plantations have had a melting-pot effect, the members of one tribe learning to live and work with the members of others. All of them say that the Lomas have the strongest medicine (occult powers used for both good and evil). Now I had said I would take one under my own roof.

'I agree for the shilling,' Comma said. He gently eased Town Chief's head off his lap to the ground and stood up. 'When I take pay, I want to give it all back to you to keep for me. I have need of much money. Much money!'

The Bassaus stared at him. Strange talk.

'What is your need?'

'I am to go to a grand school in the Gold Coast,' he said. 'I am going to be a doctor! I have a scholarship! But I must have money for clothes and there are things I must see to that have to do with my family in Lomaland.'

Johnny strode upstairs as haughtily as a plump boy can manage. I heard the kitchen door slam behind him.

Comma made friends with all the animals at once even if he could not make friends with the Bassaus. He walked around with the mongoose draped around his neck like a fur scarf and the chimps sat on his shoulders clinging tight by entwining their fingers in his hair. He treated all the animals with quiet dignity as though they were human beings too, or rather as though we were all fellow creatures. Even when the young crocodile escaped from his pool and chased the quacking ducks on a record-breaking flapping waddle around the house, the whole incident was handled without much ado. The Bassaus would have extracted the last possible whoop of excitement out of an opportunity like that!

The Bassaus ate together sitting on the ground around a

common pot of rice and soup (meat gravy). They made little balls of the mixture with their fingers and popped them into their mouths with noisy enjoyment. Comma ate with a spoon from his own bowl, sitting with a cluster of assorted animals. Comma's good will was so obvious that the Bassaus soon forgot to be afraid of him and they talked with him now and then, but they continued to exclude him at mealtime. One day when they were all under the house, I heard Johnny say, 'Comma, man, I might have a good heart for you [be fond of you] if you hadn't got yourself born a Loma!'

'I was born a Loma, Johnny,' Comma said, 'but I am a Christian now.'

'What kind of a tribe is that, the Christians?' Johnny asked. 'No tribe by that name lives in this country.'

'It is a tribe for the whole world,' Comma told him. 'It means all men are brothers.'

'They are not!' Johnny was most emphatic. 'I am a Bassau and all Bassaus are my brothers, none else! Only Bassaus! I might like some other black man, not a Bassau, small-small. But I will not like him plenty! And I hate white people, save only a few good ones. I won't be in no tribe that has got white people in it.'

'A Christian,' Comma went on to explain, 'don't go around naked, and he don't get drunk, and he eats with a spoon, and he sleeps on a bed if he can get one.'

'Oh!' Johnny seemed relieved. 'Comma, man, you swallowed the wrong word. You don't mean *Christian;* you mean *civilized.* I am civilized, only I don't like to eat with a spoon. And I don't hold still for that brother palaver!'

By payday, Comma was brother enough that they asked him to take part in the monthly celebration. Perhaps they decided that an extra shilling in the fund was reason to include him.

'Put money in the gourd, man!' Johnny approached Comma while he was swatting at the flies which torment the harness antelope. 'We make hellova play tonight! Feed the gourd with copper. Then the gourd will spit out the money to feed all we!'

Comma shook his head stubbornly. 'Thank you, Johnny. It is necessary that I save all my money.'

Johnny looked at him with pity. 'Comma,' he said, 'money is no use to a man until he spends it for something that is. You have no sense about money!'

I dreaded the 'play', knowing that Comma had lost the only opportunity he might ever get to become one of the group. It was true that he did not seem to really mind being separate. He was terribly polite to all of us in an aloof sort of way, and seemed to treasure his aloneness as an opportunity to daydream. He was thinking, I supposed, of the day when his name would be big throughout the country. The mission people thought he would make a good teacher and be of use around a hospital as a dresser or attendant, but their hopes for him were certainly not as high as his own ambition.

As soon as we had our dinner that night, the Bassaus gathered on the lawn to feast and dance and drum. After their big meal, there were a few experimental thumps on the drum. A few trial shufflings as bare feet tested the rhythm. Then Johnny, still wearing his white steward's uniform, clapped his hands for attention. Johnny's buttonholes were stretched to tearing by his swollen belly beneath. He had eaten largely. Johnny stuck out his chest and tried to pull in his overloaded abdomen. The Bassaus gathered around him expectantly. Without so much as glancing at Comma who was sitting in the doorway of his room, Johnny began his oration and delivered it in the grand manner he would have used sincerely had he been lauding a tribal hero.

'Aye, my people, listen.' They gathered into a circle around him, careful to leave a gap so Comma could see their star performer, yet not glancing toward him at any time. Johnny went on:

'Listen! This is the story of Comma. Comma was born a Loma. Now he is of the tribe of hold-tight!'

'*Aye, yah!*' Chorused with mock sorrow by the listeners.

'Comma has the closed hand. He regrets the loss of all that leaves him by the door in his backside.'

Nods from the audience. '*Aye, yah! Aye, yah!*'

'Look at the mouth of Comma. Any eye can see it has the tight look of the constipated.'

More nods of agreement. '*Aye, yah! Aye, yah!*'

'*Aye, yah! Aye,* Comma! He holds tight both ends of the food path. Comma, Comma, Comma of the closed hand.'

Having completed his eulogy, Johnny looked thoughtful, concentrated, and summoned a flatus of extravagant violence to show that he was not that sort of fellow. Then, like a chorus, anyone who was capable roared similarly. Having no firecrackers to cannon their mirth, they manufactured their own festive explosions with the machines they could manage best, their own bodies. But no matter how open-handed one's spirit (nor how well fed his insides), he cannot go on indefinitely demonstrating it in this manner. When their capacity had been exhausted, they chorused the final chant:

> *Bomaloo, Bomaloo, Bomaloo!*
> *We blow out our clothes.*
> *Roaring, roaring, roaring,*
> *We blow the dust in a cloud.*

Shrill laughter. Then someone said, 'Aye, Comma, aye, Comma!' as though he were really not such a bad sort of fellow, just stupid about money. The drums began and they danced in a circle.

Usually I enjoyed these orgies of glee on the lawn, the songs, the dances, the drum, the spontaneous eruptions of good feeling, but this one I could not endure, thinking of Comma down there on his doorstep, alone and shamed. No situation could have been a more apt illustration of a saying of Emerson's which I recalled: 'Animal spirits constitute the power of the present.' How long and at what cost could Comma deny the natural now for an improbable future? Finally I called Johnny upstairs.

'Johnny,' I said, 'you know, different people have different ideas about money. You must not hold yourself hard against Comma because he wishes to save his.'

'Comma has got the wants,' Johnny said. 'They eat a man up from the inside. Just like bug-a-bugs [termites] eat up a stick of wood! Some day, old Comma will fall down in a heap, and when he will want to stand up again, he can't because he will be nothing but a pile of sawdust. The wants will chew him into sawdust.'

'You must want some things you don't have,' I told him. 'Everyone has some wants, don't they? Comma just wants different things than you do.'

'I have got everything I need and more besides,' he said. 'I get rice because I take care of you. You sew fine clothes for me because you would feel shame if I did not look fine past all other stewards. I get sweet soap from you because when I stand behind you to brush your long hair, you do not want me to smell like a crocodile that has just eaten spoiled meat. I get enough money besides to wear a gold coat on my tooth and to buy stockfish and to make play. What more can a man want? I do not want a woman. A woman is a hellova palaver! When I need one, my father will see to it. When I want *pickins,* God and I will see to that. I live like a rich man and my insides are full and I feel fine. Old Comma down there is all dry and empty inside him.'

'What would you do if you got two shillings every day instead of one?' I asked him.

'Oh, then I would sit down half the time,' he said. 'When the moon was bright, I would dance all night and lay in hammock all day like a chief. When the moon was dark, I would work, same like now. Mommio, I want to ask you something. How is it that white people have got the wants so bad?'

'I don't know,' I said. 'I think it is catching like craw-craw [skin fungus]. They catch it from each other.'

'I would rather have craw-craw,' he said. 'It only eats people on the outside. If white people want to be old dry eaten-up sticks with sawdust and sand for insides, I don't care. But they don't need to get so hellova vexed with black people because we don't catch their old wants. That is what is wrong with Comma. He caught the wants from the white people and look where it has put him – alone in his doorway!'

'If people want to get ahead and better themselves, we call that ambition,' I told him. 'If the ambition is for good things, we think that is fine. If you wanted to be a chief, that would be your ambition. Comma's ambition is to go away to school and learn more.'

'I don't think I will hold that word, ambition, in my head, Mommio. It is a bad thing and I don't want to know it. I can say sawdust. And I don't want no sawdust for a belly. And I don't want to better myself. I like me plenty the way I am. And if I want to get ahead, my own two feet will carry me. What kind of wants have you got, Mommio?'

'I want to be happy,' I said. It sounded pretty silly after I said it, but it was the truth.

'Oh, Mommio,' he said, 'I know that a trouble sits on you these days. Now I have not got as plenty in my head as you, but I can throw you some sense about how to be glad. All you got to do is let go, and be!'

Johnny cleared his throat and gave me a roguish grin. 'Now I will tell you my ambition! My ambition is that you should get out that book, the one where you say you write down the sense we tell you. Write in that book that Johnny says that Comma's wants will take him into trouble. You know Town Chief has got the wants for wine. You know the palaver he sees and all of us see because of that one small thing. But wine is a small want if you lay it beside Comma's big wants. When Comma's big wants bring trouble to plenty people, you will look back in the book and read what Johnny said, and the way it would be for true, for true. Now you know my *ambition!*'

'So I will do,' I promised him. 'Now I will tell you my ambition. You go downstairs and ask Comma if he has got sticks or legs. By that, he will know that you will allow him to dance with you.'

'All right, Mommio,' he agreed. 'I will ask him. Poor old sand and sawdust Comma!'

When I looked out of the window, Comma was not dancing but he had manned the largest drum and he was making it talk with such vigour that not even a strident Bassau could have wished for more.

III

TRUTH IS ALL OF ONE PIECE

It is the badness inside a man that burns him.

TRIAL BY SASSWOOD is an ordeal in which an accused person drinks an infusion made from the poisonous bark of the sasswood tree. If he is guilty, the poison will 'catch' him, he will die. If he is not guilty, his stomach will acquit him. Vomiting establishes innocence. In common speech, *sasswood* has come to apply to any form of trial by ordeal, and there are many. Plucking a brass anklet from the bottom of a potful of (apparently) boiling palm oil is a popular variety in general use. It was this kind of trial which Comma wished to stand.

Several white persons have witnessed trials by ordeal in Liberia; a few have written about them. I have never discussed the matter with anyone who did not try to explain them away. 'The oil was not really boiling,' they say. Or, 'The cutlass was not really red hot.' (In hot-cutlass sasswood, a blade is heated in the fire and stroked across the bare backs of all the suspects. Only the guilty one is supposed to be burned.) If the trial has taken the form of drinking the red water, the brew of the sasswood bark, the usual comment, if the accused survives, is that the infusion was too weak to be fatal. If the victim dies, the explanation made is that he was a nuisance so the concoction was made purposely into fatal dosage. There is always from white people the suggestion that the trial was rigged. I grant that the possibilities for this are numerous and probably abused.

Ask the sceptics, 'Do you believe that Hindu holy men can

33

walk through live coals without feeling pain? Or that Indian dentists can pull teeth without the patient feeling discomfort?' 'Some sort of hypnosis,' they answer as though giving it a recognizable name diminished the wonder of it. 'Hypnosis must be the explanation of trials by ordeal.'

Regardless of what one may choose to believe about these matters, there is one point on which everyone seems to agree: *the trials work for the Africans because they have implicit faith in them.* I have never heard of a tribesman questioning the verdict of sasswood.

An American doctor once established the potency of an infusion of sasswood bark. His sample came from a potful of the brew from which an accused old woman drank considerably more than a lethal dose. She evidenced her innocence and showed not the slightest ill effects. He observed that she gulped it down with complete confidence. It was his opinion that a smaller dose of the same strength, sipped haltingly and reluctantly by a victim who knew he was guilty, might have been retained and absorbed, resulting in death.

It seemed likely to me that if Comma had stolen, his hand, reaching for the anklet in the bottom of the pot, would fumble nervously and be immersed for a longer interval than otherwise. If he were innocent? The possibility of serious burns plagued me as I prepared for the trip. I had seen a native boy in his own village stand under twenty-five lashes across his bare back before he fainted. His crime? Stealing a ha'p'ny! Hinterland Africans who have never been out of their own villages would rather one of their boys died under the lash than live to thieve. Association with coastal life disintegrates their high standards of honesty rather quickly.

I began to have nightmares in which I saw Comma's raised hand, horribly burned. His hands were long from wrist to knuckles, long in the fingers, too, and thin-through. When he folded his fingers back against themselves, the whole seemed no thicker than Johnny's pudgy little fist extended.

Looking at Comma's hands when he was using them, plaiting a raffia rope, weaving a bamboo sleeping-mat, flicking a drum, one became more than usually aware of the mechanism of sinew and tendon and bone under the tight casing of skin. Thinking of that thin hand, its regrettable absence of an insulating layer of fat, the thin wrist where the pulse vessel stood out in tracery with the small branches showing like tiny twigs, my nightmares became day-horrors.

I began to question my motives. I wanted to help Comma clear his name. But I had no assurance, none whatever, that the trial would contribute to that. What about my insatiable curiosity about everything native? Wasn't that one of the reasons I had consented to trip and trial? I sent Johnny over to the hospital with a note asking for a large jar of tannic acid jelly. Feeling guilty, I went on with the packing.

'Mommio,' Johnny asked me as he wrapped up the bedding, 'do you know why I go to the clubhouse with you when the Bishop comes to hold church for the white peoples?'

'I think you like to see him standing up there fine and straight with his white hair and his purple robe,' I said. 'And when he takes off the ɔbe, you like to take care of it for him.'

'I like that all right,' he admitted. 'But that is not my big reason. I want to hear what white mens believe so I can understand why they act like they do.'

'Well, what do you make of it?'

'I don't make sense, I tell you that, Mommio. The thinks and the acts have got a big swamp between and no way to cross over.'

'Such as?'

'Well, I heard Bishop Kroll say that the only bad thing any man needs to fear is the bad that is inside him.'

'That is true,' I said. 'I believe that.'

'You say it is true, but you don't *believe* it is true, Mommio. That is one of the matters with white people. They don't believe what they say they believe. The say-es and the thinks-es and the does-es are stranger, all stranger.'

'Why do you say that I don't believe the Bishop, Johnny?'

'All right! I'll tell you. You know that story of Shadrach and those other two boys that got put in the fire? I got Comma to read me that story like you told me I should. Comma said it came out of your God-book, the same one the Bishop holds in his hand with all the bright ribbons spilling out of it. Well, those boys didn't even get their clothes turned brown in the heat BECAUSE THERE WAS NO BAD IN THEM! What about the mens that dumped them in the fire? They got all burned up so none could tell which had been which. That was because they were bad mens. It is just like our trials with the burning oil and the hot cutlasses. *It is the badness inside a man that burns him!*'

'And you think I don't believe that?' (I didn't, not literally, and Johnny knew it.)

'No, you don't believe it. You put that hellova can of medicine-for-burns in the chest. I asked the dresser at the hospital what it was and he told me. Your says-es and your does-es are stranger for true. Sometimes, I don't even know your thinks-es.'

'You know too many of my thinks-es,' I said. 'I don't always like it.'

'Oh, well,' he comforted me, 'most time they are fair-good. No mind!'

'Don't you believe that sasswood ever catches a good person, Johnny?'

'It never does! Because no person is altogether good. Some just are not so bad as others. Suppose a man dies in a village. All the people want to know what killed him. Everyone knows that this person and that person and some other person held something hard in their hearts against this dead man. When they have palaver, they vex and they wish the man dead. All right! They have all helped to kill him. If the sasswood catches any of the people that have wished the man dead, they have caught the right one.

'A person has got to be careful about bad thinks,' Johnny went on. 'Sometimes a bad think can get loose out of you without you know it. It grows and gets more strong after it gets out. It can go around hurting people bad, bad, and you can never get it back again to step on it.'

What Johnny was telling me was something I had heard many times from the Africans – any evil impulse emanating from a person takes on a vigorous and separate entity once it has left its origin, and even though you never know all its foul acts you are still morally (and legally) liable because you 'borned it', it came out of you.

'When we are on the trail,' I told him, 'and we tell stories at night around the fire, I will tell you our story that is like that. It is about Pandora's box.'

'Don't tell me no more stories you don't believe, Mommio. I like on my tongue the taste of stories I can swallow down. The reason to tell stories is to say a true, true thing that you do not know any other way to say! White people tell stories just to give each other belly-laughs. That is a wrong-thing to do with a story.'

I do not think that Johnny was any more anti-white than the average black on the plantation. He was just more out-spoken about it. He knew that the causes of racial friction were of deepest interest to me and he obliged by pointing them out. When he spoke his antagonisms he seldom extended his bitterness to me personally. It was as though he and I were of some neutral tint standing outside the arena of hostilities, interested spectators but not participants. I had lost that neutrality for the time being by sending him for that jar of ointment. To him this belied that I believed there was any inherent or protecting power in goodness.

'Suppose,' I asked him, 'that you are boiling our drinking water before you pour it in the filter. It rolls over the top on your hand. Won't it burn you whether you have lied or not?'

'That is not a test of truth,' he said. 'That is only a test of whether you are too lazy to watch the kettle. God don't bother to watch a man boil drinking water, which is a lot of humbug anyway. But God has got an eye on you hard when you stand before the boiling oil in a sasswood trial!'

A heaviness in me made the packing seem weary going. It was worry, I think, about how the undertaking would end. So many times in Africa when a white person meddles with a bad situation, the muddle only thickens, no matter how good his intentions. The preparations should have been easy. Under the house stood the tier of wooden cases which had gone down the narrow jungle trails ahead of me so many times in the past two years. Inside the lid of each was a typed list, splotched with mildew now but still legible enough, of the necessities that should go into each box – the medicines, the ammunition, the gifts, the trade goods, the clothing, the few books I would want to read, the kerosene, the lanterns——

As Johnny and Comma and I worked under the house sorting the trail supplies, the air was spiced by chill and damp and a screen of quiet rain hung a grey drapery around the perimeter of the eaves. Now and then one of the men Zabogi had chosen for a carrier would step like a ghost through that fluid curtain-wall, streaming water and apologizing, but begging for an advance on his carrying wages because, of course, he could not return to his people without a cargo of gifts.

Comma annoyed Johnny by insisting on reading aloud and checking off the lists on the box-lids. Johnny, who could not read one word, knew each box by some scar of the trail, some dent whose origin he remembered fondly from other trips. He knew exactly what had been the contents of each and how they had been packed. Comma's accountant manner of inventory was an affront to Johnny's stewardship.

'When a person learns to read his head gets to be a sieve. Everything good and useful runs through it like palm oil,' Johnny grumbled. 'Only the husks remain. I remember what goes where and I don't need a paper to tell me.'

Comma was usually patient with Johnny in a superior sort of way, but now our ankles were chilled from standing on the damp earth and the boys were overwrought with the excitement of the journey, and the chimpanzees had been a nuisance all afternoon. Every time one of us put something in a box and turned to pick up something else, their curious little heads were peering into the carton and they busied themselves scrambling the contents. Johnny felt Comma had better apply his talent to diverting the animals and leave the packing to an old master hand like himself.

'You are just jealous because you can't read and write, Johnny,' Comma accused him. 'Now I could never be a doctor if——'

'Humph!' Johnny glared at him. 'There is just one reason I don't want to learn book.'

'You are too lazy, that's the reason.' Comma was still remote and superior.

'I would learn if I wanted to,' Johnny said with spirit. 'I do not think it is hard to put reading in your head. I can read your arm already.'

Sometime before I knew him, Comma had, at considerable cost of pain to himself, made a decorative row of scars in the form of commas down his left forearm. The circles were as large as a quarter and bright indigo in colour. The stems of the symbol were uncertain wiggles and weaker in scarification, trailing off in colour to his natural coppery tint.

'That is not reading, Johnny, to know a comma when you see one.' Comma ran his forefinger over the bright welts.

'It is so,' Johnny retorted. 'The books upstairs have got plenty commas inside. You yourself told me that when you see a comma without a tail, it means to stop. But when the tail is there, it means to give pause and hang head [think]. The tail on a comma is your neck, and the round part is your head bent over in a think. But the trouble with people who can read is that when they hang head for a think, the good sense runs out. Look at your arm. See how thin is the part that means the neck. Big heads and thin necks, that is what books do to people! But I will tell you this! I will learn to write if black people get so stupid that they all learn to read.'

'What has that got to do with it?' Comma asked him icily. 'Some day all black people will know how to read and write both.'

'When black people can read, then I will learn to write.' Johnny put his hands on his hips, elbows akimbo, and thrust his head forward. 'I will write all the truth I know about white people. I will tell the black ones that white people do not believe what their own tongues say, so why should anyone else believe them? I will write that white people do not do what their own hearts tell them, so why should black people do what white people tell them? If a white person ever shows me how to write and all the black ones how to read, all the white mens in the world will get sorry for it!'

'It is no good to read or write unless you read and write what is good,' I said. 'If you make trouble with books, it is better not to have books.'

'The only trouble books will make in this country is trouble for white mens!' Johnny's eyes gleamed as though he were seeing the trouble in a crystal ball of thoughts. 'I would let my head get made into an old rusty sieve that can't hold nothing in it if I could do that.'

'Johnny,' I said. 'Would you hold your heart hard against me as you are doing now if my skin were black?'

'Yes, I would!' he said pertly. 'But then if your skin were black, you would *believe* that GOOD is medicine enough for anyone! And no help from medicine from the hospital!' He relaxed his bellicose stance then and laughed a little sheepishly.

'But Mommio, I would love you if your skin was green as a gecko!'

'Johnny,' Comma said, 'you talk too much.'

'And you, Comma, you read too plenty! Old sieve-head, big-head! Go hang your head in a think. And then go hang it in the rain for shame. Give me that lantern you forgot to clean.'

Comma handed over the smoked lantern. He was laughing now too that the tension was relieved. 'Why, Johnny,' he said, 'you are a poet. A Bassau-English poet.'

'I am not,' Johnny said. 'I am a steward, and a plenty-good one, and I don't forget to clean lanterns.

'Who is going to carry the money box?' Johnny asked me. 'Will Zabogi name the man?'

'Will the chest be locked?' Johnny asked this slowly as though it mattered a great deal.

'It will not,' I said. 'Unless Comma wishes to lock it when we sit down in the villages for the night. He will carry the key.'

'Oh, Mommio!' Johnny was radiant now. 'You are putting your thinks-es and your does-es in one piece again. You *act* now like you think Comma never thieved from you even if you don't believe about Shadrach and that GOOD inside a man will keep him from hurt outside. I go now, make hot coffee for you.'

'Oh, Johnny,' Comma moaned, holding out his hands, palms up, and looking at them reproachfully as though they should have remembered of themselves what they were supposed to do without reference to his preoccupied head. 'I forgot to beat the coffee beans in the mortar.'

'Go then, beat them now,' Johnny ordered him. 'Old sieve-head, big-head, small in the neck!'

'The chimpanzees carried the mortar, Johnny. They lost it out there in the rain, somewhere.'

'Long time since,' Johnny said scathingly, 'chimpanzees

studied to learn book. They have been no use ever after. This one time, I will go beat the coffee in my own mortar. But only this once!'

He bustled off to his own room to get the little mortar he kept there, swathed in a clean towel. The screen door banged behind him. Johnny bristled with purposeful energy. Whether he was working or eating or dancing he was all sputter and sparks like a Fourth of July fizz-stick. Comma, when observed by himself, seemed to possess the quiet grace of a wild thing and to accomplish his task with an economy of movement and a delicacy of touch. But when he was with Johnny, the contrast made him seem insolently languorous.

'Comma,' I said, 'why did you have those blue scars made on your arm?'

He ran his fingertips over them wistfully.

'I wanted to be marked. The other boys in my village all had the marks of the Poro cut into their skins when they went to the Bush School. The mission would not agree for the Devil to eat me.'

The 'Devil's tooth-marks' are the rows of scars cut into the skins of the initiates of the Poro or Devil's Bush, the secret cult society for male tribesmen.

'So,' he continued, 'I burned the mark of my learning into my skin. *A man has got to belong to something!* I belong to learning. I must always hold that thought.'

'Comma, you understand, don't you, that sasswood trials carry no weight with white people?'

'You will love my mother,' he said emphatically.

Africans have a way of veering like this. At first, it seems they are dodging the subject you want to discuss. It is very annoying until you learn to recognize it as a gap in the conversation. After one understands this, he learns that these blanks are the most important part. If you can figure out what has not been said and fit it in where it belongs with what was said, the seemingly unrelated fragments of a jigsaw assemble into a complete picture. What Comma had said was a clue to me that his mother was part of the key to the riddle of what had happened to him.

'Won't you fear when the time comes to plunge your arm into the pot?' I asked him. 'You will smell the hot oil and see the blue smoke coming out of it and the red fire under it. Won't you be sorry then that you begged to be put to that test?'

'I will no more fear to put my hand to the bottom of the kettle than I fear to put it out there in the rain.' There was a ring of conviction in his voice.

'If you will change your mind, Comma, there is still time. We don't have to go through with this.'

'Why should I change my mind, Mommio? Do you think Shadrach went to the furnace with fear in his heart?'

'Shadrach is a story out of the Old Testament,' I protested feebly. 'Sasswood is out of tribal religion.'

'It is the same, Mommio. They are both truth and truth is all of one piece!'

IV

THE WORLD IS HOW BIG?

*A thing has no weight in the hand if it can
be lifted for nothing.*

THE CARRIERS walked through the rain in the night to be
at my house by sun-up on the morning we were to leave.
Some of them could have been picked up en route to
Salala, the end of the motor road, but they would walk any
distance they could ride back. Nor would they have wished
to miss the hubbub of group departure. I heard their lively
chatter under the house while I ate my breakfast.

'Fine weather to drown!' Zabogi announced cheerfully.
Tama's giggle blended with their deep chuckles. The mention
of drowning reminded Johnny that he had overheard Ants
wish that fate on me. He added a few embellishments as he
told them about it. They had a delicious time, then, making
wishes for Ants. Decapitating and stabbing were discarded as
showing lack of imagination. In rapid succession, he was
subjected to a miscellany of more colourful and anguished
ends. First, he was tied to a tree in line of march of the biggest
blackest mass of driver ants ever to cross Africa. They released
him from the tree because that had been done to people
before, although in the past the ants had not had jaws as big
as a cow's. Better to dig a pit and put him in it with a hungry
python. The python was to be long enough to reach from
Sierra Leone to the Ivory Coast and half-way back again. It
was to have sufficient strength in its coils to crunch a big old
sasswood tree off at the base with one squeeze. When all of

Ants' bones were crushed they would pitch him a few coppers to heal him. After this show of mercy, they would drag him from the python's unhinged jaws after only his head had been engulfed. He was astonishingly elongated after the python had him in condition to swallow. It was considerable bother to fold him up like a length of cloth and stuff him in a leopard trap for live bait. With fiendish glee they turned beaters to shoo a man-eating leopard toward the trap. They went thoroughly into the spirit of the chase, slapping their clothes, pounding the ground with sticks, and shouting advice to the leopard about what parts of the man's anatomy to nibble first. When I came down the stairs, their eyes were glowing with the excitement of the chase and the kill. Only Comma stood aside, nervously fingering the tattooed scars on his arm. The oval of his face seemed to thin and elongate in unease.

'If the leopard is at the trap, we will go now,' I told them.

Zabogi rushed over to the foot of the stairs and saluted smartly. 'Aye, Mommio, all we ready! Make go! Ants can wait. Leopard whiskers take time.'

Zabogi meant to say that revenge can always wait on tomorrow and tomorrow. Leopard whiskers chopped into tiny fragments are sometimes slipped into an enemy's food. They promote the growth of cysts in the digestive tract, acting like sand in an oyster. After the long and uncomfortable time it takes these growths to fill the stomach, the victim dies. A man's revenge 'tastes better after a long chewing'.

'A walk to Lomaland takes a couple of sundowns, too,' I said. 'Let's go!'

They thought this was uproariously funny. Understatement amuses them as much as exaggeration.

'Wait small, Zabogi,' Comma requested. 'I have got to give good-bye to the animals.'

The upswung laugh-creases in Zabogi's full face all reversed direction. Zabogi's mobile features reminded me of the conventional theatre masks for Comedy and Tragedy.

His could be either within the flicker of a thought. In anger he looked as though he had just exhausted himself with a sob and had not recovered enough breath to haul the heavy thickness of his big rubbery lips back to a normal horizontal bulge. Whatever he said to Comma was growled in Loma. The others took up the mutter.

Zabogi was determined that we were going to reach Sanoyea, the next village beyond Salala, before sundown He was not willing to be delayed by any sentiment toward animals on the part of Comma. It is possible to walk from Salala to Sanoyea in one day, but anyone who has ever done it will agree that it is an unhuman way to treat yourself, even when the paths are dry and the streams are nothing more than silvery trickles between mossy boulders.

Comma took estimate of Zabogi's stern expression. Then his look appealed to me to intervene. I looked at my feet, which is a way to say, 'This is not my palaver.' Everyone watched while Comma went, with what seemed deliberate tardiness, from chimpanzee to chimpanzee, patting each of them on the head. He shook hands with Town Chief, whose personality had become more integrated after Comma had weaned him from alcohol. The chimps seemed to understand that we were leaving and their mournful little mugs were more melancholy than ever.

Still moving slowly, Comma turned toward Zabogi. 'I ready now,' he said. I don't know what I expected Zabogi to do about this insubordination, but I certainly expected that he would do something. Nor do I know what the others were thinking but I could tell they were nervous because Tama tittered until Zabogi glared her into silence. The men just scuffed their great toes in the dust.

'Let go!' Zabogi roared. He was smiling a little to himself. If anyone could put Mona Lisa's expression on features like this, he had almost accomplished it. 'Oh, God,' I thought, 'he's chewing his anger. If only he had spit it out now before we start.' The loads were all in the pick-ups. We piled in ourselves, and the chimps, sure now that we were leaving, set up such an uproar of lament that it was impossible to hear the motors of the cars as we careened out of the drive, the loose gravel flying out from the tyres towards the huddles of hairy screaming little creatures.

No one but myself seemed to think there was anything ludicrous about our entourage: fifteen boys who had clamoured and contested to walk through rain-drenched jungle for a week or more with forty-pound loads atop. Zabogi, all chiefly zest, going home to prove he could chief a frisky woman! Tama, gloriously decked out from the waist down in a bright new golden wrap-around *lappa,* and from the waist up in nothing except her too-evident pride in being a desired woman! Comma, exhilarated and proud, because this trip was being made for him, and would end beside a smoking pot of hot oil into which he would be allowed to plunge his arm. Myself, cast in the role of official accuser, when my only wish was to establish innocence!

We dismounted at Salala and ducked for shelter on to the porch of my friend Baysah's store. Rain was falling, not violently but thickly and unslanted. All of the wooden cases wore hats. These were cone-shaped, plaited out of palm leaves, and as wide at the bottom as a man's shoulders. Roof-for-head, they are called, but for all the heads except my own and Zabogi's, there would be a head-load between head and hat. Tama was elected to carry the cumbersome bundle made up of all the gifts the carriers were taking to their people. As these included a couple of roosters, the total was too awkward for her to balance on her head. While I went in to greet Baysah, the carriers set about making her a carrying cradle of palm leaves, called a *kinja,* to fit on her back.

Baysah was a misplaced Loma (Salala being in Kpuesi territory), and a wily trader. He had located at a strategic spot. Salala is in the crutch of a 'Y'. We had come up the short stem on the motor road. The long right arm of the 'Y' goes to Ganta and French Guinea. That trail was familiar to me. The longer left arm, the one we would travel, led to Loma country. All the merchandise going up or down country to either place passed by Baysah's piazza, and much of it rested there long enough to suffer a steep rise in price.

Baysah had one back room he had never let me see. He was highly mysterious about it and always managed to stand between me and the curtain which separated it from the counter room. He hoarded peanuts in there, for one thing. Sometimes after he had sold me what he insisted was his entire supply, he would duck in there and bring out another basket of them if I, as my trump card in the constant haggle to get food, could produce an American magazine.

These magazines had varying trade value without regard to age, condition, or literary merit. Only Baysah knew how he weighed their worth in peanuts. 'Not worth peanuts' takes on a different meaning in Liberia because when the hunting has been bad, they are the only acceptable solution to the protein problem. Made into a thick gravy, they are very good with rice.

'That one, madam,' Baysah said one time after I had brought him an only two months old *Atlantic Monthly,* 'is not worth even one peanut with a worm inside.' *Esquire* and the *New Yorker* would usually get me two 'government cans' (number two tin cans with the bottoms slightly rounded down). Sometimes a copy of *Time* was acceptable and sometimes it was not. The one sure way to open the cornucopia of the back room was to produce an issue of *Life*. But two copies at one time were not twice as valuable as one.

I was as curious about how Baysah established the relative worth of these publications as I was about the secret chamber. Sometimes I heard strange noises coming from behind the curtain. There was laughter and low moaning and exclamations of surprise and delight. I had never heard of a brothel in the interior of Liberia but I began to wonder.

'Baysah,' I teased him once after I had told him some fairy-tales in exchange for his folk-stories, 'I think you are an old Bluebeard, and do away with your wives in that room, there.'

'I haven't any beard,' he said, 'and I haven't any wives. If I had a beard it wouldn't be blue, and if I had any wives they wouldn't be in there. They would be in the rice-farm by day, and in the kitchen until after chop [food or eating]. After chop, well, it depends. . . .' He flashed his gold tooth in a sly grin.

'I can't figure you out,' I told him. 'Sometimes I think you love learning, and sometimes I think you love money.'

'I love all two, both,' he said. 'A man does not have to love one and leave the other. Of what use is learning if it does not put coppers in the kettle?'

'Many people who have learning feel they should use it to help other people.' This sounded smug to me and as soon as I had said it I wished that I had not.

'True!' he agreed emphatically, taking no offence. 'I use my learning to instruct all the people in this village and any who pass through and want to be instructed. You must know though, madam, that some people do not wish to be instructed. All who take sense from me pay for it. They pay plenty. Else, my instruction would have no value. A thing has no weight in the hand if it can be lifted for nothing.'

'Suppose I gave you the magazines I bring here and did not take pay in peanuts?' I asked him. 'Would the magazines have less value because they were free?'

'I would want and respect the magazines just the same,' he said. 'I would take all I could get out of you. But I would lose respect for you. I would wonder what it was you wanted out of me and I would think up suspicions to put on you. As it is, we look each other straight in the eye. That is one of the crazies about white people. They want you to like them because they give you something! When a white man gives something to a black man, he wants us to show all our teeth

in a hellova grin and say, "Thank you, boss." Why should
he be thanked when the only person he has made feel good
is his own self!'

'Don't you ever give a gift, Baysah? I don't mean the *dash*
[the something extra that accompanies every transaction and is
on both sides]. I mean a gift that has nothing to do with a deal.'

'I have too much sense to do it very often,' he said. 'When
I do it, it is because I am going to get myself something for
it later. That later business is no good. It makes palaver. It is all
right to put off the pay but not the price! When you are giving
someone something for nothing, you are putting his buttock
on the ground while you take the chair. (Chiefs have chief-
chairs, respected elders have low stools, men of standing sit
on mats, slaves and despised people must sit on the bare earth.'

'Every time you add to a gift,' Baysah went on, 'you are
putting longer legs under your chair. Even a big chief knows
enough to keep his chair low. When the white man's chair
gets too high, the legs will wobble. Some day the white man
will fall off on his face and break his head.' Baysah's face lit
up as though he were at that moment witnessing this satisfying
spectacle.

'And you will be glad, Baysah? Why?'

'Sure, I will be glad,' he said. 'You don't have to call a man
boss when he has got a broken head.'

'Well, ' I said, not wishing to discuss race with him when
he was in that mood, 'you hold the chair as long as you get
first chance at all the peanuts that come down country. And
I am on a mat out in the hot sun with a beat-up old magazine.'

'Give me one paper for free, and I am down on a mat
too.' He laughed now and slapped his stomach but it was not
a hearty free laugh. There was something nervous and greedy
about it. I believe he was laughing at a mental picture of
himself being abject before a white woman for the sake of
profitable barter.

'Nothing doing!' I said. 'You can give me two cans of

peanuts and keep your behind up high!' Then Baysah laughed again and this time it was a real laugh. That is how it was to visit with Baysah. The most I could expect from him was a measured respect; I did not hope for affection or loyalty. With Johnny, hating the white race in general and adoring a few of them in particular was an emotional luxury in which he indulged himself. Baysah's hatred was a different kind which would never entirely excuse my own lack of colour. It was a slow-grinding kind of hatred that seemed to pulverize all his thinking about any subject into separate little gritty particles.

While we jostled over the rutted road to Salala, I thought that Baysah, being a big man among the Lomas, probably enjoyed Comma's confidence. He might give me a few cryptic clues before I started the trek. As soon as the carriers began to plait Tama's *kinja,* I went inside the store and sat down on the worn unpainted counter. Baysah came from behind the blue-and-white country cloth curtain to greet me. I noticed that the white stripes in the edge of the curtain were dark and crusty with soil as though hundreds of greasy hands had swept them aside. Even the dark blue indigo stripes were darkened and glazed with a waxy sheen of dirt. In Baysah's hand was a worn copy of *Time.*

Baysah shook hands with me without smiling enough to show even the bottom edge of his gold tooth. 'I see,' he said, dolefully, 'that summer is gone.' His expression registered this as catastrophic news.

'Summer?' What could Baysah understand of summer when it was all he had ever known? On the plantation, the leaves of the rubber trees colour up brilliantly for a short time, and are just as briefly bare before new leaves burst out all over them, but that is the only hint of seasons, other than wet and dry.

'Summer?' I said again, blankly.

'Sure!' Baysah snapped. 'Summer in your State Department. All right! I will tell you, who ought to be telling me! The big men in your country do not agree and Summer

walked out on the palaver. That's a hellova thing for a war
when the chiefs who are on the same side can not agree.'

'Oh! Sumner Welles!'

'That's the one I said!' Baysah was completely out of
patience with me. 'Now this Summer, he was plenty good
at throwing cold water on hot palaver. How will the war go
on without him? Will the fighting spread now and catch up
here in Salala? If the war comes down across French Africa
like some say it will, it will come right through here to get
the rubber on the plantation, right through Salala. The path
is past my store.'

'The war will go on,' I assured him, 'but if it comes to the
plantation, I think it will come by sea and not by Salala. An
army cannot move over a trail through the jungle. Even
without Mr. Welles in a chief-chair, the war will go on.
Throwing cold water on the hot palavers comes after the guns
are laid down. The easy words come after the shooting stops.'

'That is wrong, all wrong, back-ways,' Baysah said, glumly.
'The chiefs should use all their words before they use guns.'
I saw that the end of the cigarette I had given him was damp
and chewed. I had brought the war to Salala in a magazine.

Out on the piazza, the carriers were having a merry time
getting the trussed-up roosters on top of Tama's head.

'Shut up, out there!' Baysah yelled at the doorway. Then
he turned to me again. 'The world is how big? And how
much of it does the war cover now? And how long did the
war take to cover that much?'

Baysah looked so wretched I thought he must be seeing
the globe with war flowing over it like paint in a Sherwin
Williams ad and that he was trying to compute by mathe-
matical progression how long it would be before he and his
store were blotted out under the flow. And how should I tell
him the size of the world? The word 'mile' would have no
meaning for him. Liberians measure distance to a given point
by how many sundowns they have to walk to reach it.

'How big do you think the world is, Baysah?' I hoped to distract him from his uneasiness, to put something a little more friendly between us.

'I used to think,' he said, 'that the world was as big as the distance from where I was to the farthest place where a man I know has his house. I know a Mandingo trader. He carries goat-hair blankets from way back of Sierra Leone to the Ivory Coast. He brings back a head-load of carved ivory bangles. He has got a house and a set of wives and many children at both ends of the trail. He stops here at night and we sit late. He tells me about both places and all that is in between. So I thought the world started where his wives weave goat-hair blankets and ended in the courtyard where the ivory carvers sit to file the bangles. Farther than that all there was of the world was grey to me, and nothing it in. It was like a cloud sitting down on empty land.

'All right! That world was big enough! Then you brought me papers which I could read if I took a long time to it, and put my finger under every word. That way, the white people's country got into the world for me. I could sit down more easy before that happened. Now they are in my world and their war is in it, too, and I can't get it out, even in my sleep. Then there is that road they are going to build to Ganta! My store won't be the end of the road any more. Everyone and everything stops at the end of a road, but no one will stop when I am only a small place beside the road. All will pass me by!'

'When you first learned to read,' I asked him, 'didn't that spread your world beyond Sierra Leone and the Ivory Coast?'

'It did not,' he said. 'The missionary who taught me to read taught me from the Bible. That was just like reading about our own people. They had tribes and chiefs and rain-makers and many wives and goats and they hated government tax collectors! They kept people with leprosy outside the villages and they liked bright coats and they had drums and if the chief did not hold them hard, they broke the laws. They acted just like Lomas. Those are plenty-fine stories in the Bible.'

'You told me once you had no time for stories,' I said. 'You wouldn't give me even one peanut with a worm inside it for a very fine magazine when you flipped the pages and saw that it had stories in it.'

'I don't need to wear my fingernail short spelling out white men's stories. I know better ones and I don't have to read them, either. I think of just two things when you bring me papers. One is how many facts are in it that I can store up in my head. The other is how much copper it will put in my kettle.'

There was a crash out on the porch as of a carton falling. Silence, then titters. Baysah strode to the door.

'More palaver out there and I will throw you out in the mud,' he threatened them. 'Sit easy now. Zabogi, come inside, man, if you want.' Even Baysah seemed to feel he should defer to Zabogi (though not to Comma, I noticed). To my relief, Zabogi shook his head and stood where he was.

'Do you sell the papers, Baysah? How can they put coppers in the kettle?'

'If you knew what a fine thing I make of them you would demand too many peanuts.' He was rubbing the tips of his fingers together the way he always did when money was discussed.

'If I promise not to hold you to a harder bargain? Will you tell me, then?'

'Promise with your tongue on sasswood?'

'On sasswood,' I said.

'All right, then! I'll show you.'

Baysah swept aside the soiled curtains and for the first time I entered the mysterious chamber. *Kinjas* full of produce were stacked along the sides. In the centre of the back wall were four little cubicles about the size of telephone booths, curtained on three sides with lengths of country cloth. The fronts were open. In each one, about waist-high, was a crude shelf, and on each shelf was a copy of *Life*.

'It costs one copper for anyone to stand there while the sand runs through the small hole in the bottom of my time-keeper gourd,' Baysah explained. 'You see now why the picture-books get you more peanuts. I am the only man in this village who can read words, but anyone can read pictures.'

And, I had suspected that Baysah was running a brothel!

'But the other magazines,' I asked him, 'the *New Yorker* and *Esquire*? What do you do with them? They have stories in them and you say our stories are not worth the wearing off of a fingernail to spell out.'

'Oh, those!' He seemed a little shy now, and not wanting to tell me, but not knowing how to get out of it. 'Well, I like them for the big bright come-buys [ads]. I see a big ol' shoe and I think how much more fine that shoe would look if it had my foot inside it. I read my wishes in those books! But, they are dangerous, very dangerous! They could put money out of my pocket, not put it in!

'Now that Comma,' Baysah went on, 'that is the trouble with him. He doesn't think how to make his learning put money in his pocket and keep it there. He has got a big hungry for money so he can spend it to put more learning in his head. If he had sense, he would make the learning that he has already got bring money to him, the way I do here. Comma has got his ideas backwards.'

'Do you think Comma stole that money, Baysah?' We were alone in the dim room with the main store between us and the carriers.

'Comma did not steal! All he did was lie. It was not a clever lie he told you. If he had asked me, I would have tailored him a better one.'

'Why don't you tell me what really happened, Baysah? Then I wouldn't need to walk all the way to Lomaland in the rain.'

'Oh, you want to go,' Baysah told me. 'Else you wouldn't

it do. Anyhow the truth is not the same in different places. Truth about anything is true only where it happened. It would seem different here in this room. It wouldn't taste good and you couldn't swallow it. Comma is keeping the truth under his shirt until you reach Lomaland.'

'We say "under your hat".' Baysah was interested in mastering our idioms, and I thought he had confused that one.

'I don't mean in his head, only. Have you seen him without his shirt since the money was lost?'

Thinking about it, then, I could not remember that I had.

The carriers were getting restless. The planks of the piazza floor were creaking as a heavy weight paced their length, Zabogi impatient to get going. Sanoyea was a long way up the path.

'I go now, Baysah,' I said.

'Mommio?' He had never called me that before. Usually, it was madam, or good friend.

'Yes, Baysah?'

'Mommio, I want to give you my blessing for the journey.'

I bowed my head for an instant so he would know that I wanted his blessing to rest on me. Then I stepped off his piazza into the rain and the carriers queued up behind, Johnny nearest me, then Tama, then Comma, and after the carrying-men, Zabogi. They were all strangely quiet as they stepped into line as though there were something solemn about the moment of leaving. The only sound I heard was the slather of rain over the thatch of my roof-for-head.

On a little rise of ground where the path disappears under the arched branches of the high trees, we turned to wave at Baysah. He was standing on his piazza, his posture drooped and slack, flapping the limp magazine in farewell.

'That Baysah is all eaten out with the wants,' Johnny said. 'He has got the white peoples' wants, just like you, Comma. The wants sure dry up the laughs.'

'Sh!' Comma tried to hush him. 'This is not the place to talk that one.'

'I will not shush,' Johnny retorted. 'Any place is the place to say a truth like that. I have never been to Lomaland, but I know that when I leave the plantation to go to Bassau country, the farther I put the plantation behind me, the less people want and the more they laugh. Now that old Baysah! He is all the time sour and vexed because a road is going beyond Salala. He says it will hurt him and spoil his business. But I will tell you what people the road will hurt and spoil. It will hurt all the people it reaches. The wants can't walk a trail but they sure can travel a road!'

Through the blur of rain, I could see that Baysah was shivering in the early morning cold. I knew that when he went back inside his dirty shop, empty of people now, he would not feel its cosy warmth. The dusty smell of hampers of rice and the rich oily odour of unroasted peanuts and the yeasty bubbling of palm wine would not hearten him because the alien disturbing smell of printer's ink had been added to these familiar other smells. And he knew that the forest wall against which his little mud shop was snuggled was going to be felled through for a road which would connect with other roads, far away and already built, to him a ruinous network spun out over a world getting larger by the hour.

Road machinery and printing presses were pushing back the walls that bounded Baysah's thinking and the world was swollen in size beyond his wildest imaginings. The newly opened spaces were bound to be uncomfortable and draughty until he could get used to wider dimensions.

In America, we were and still are, trying to get adjusted to the pinches of a *shrinking* globe. How then should I have answered Baysah when he asked me, 'How big is the world?' Miles never had any significance to him and they no longer have any to us. Didn't he give me the right measure when he said, 'The world is as big as the distance from where I sit to the farthest place where a man I know has his house. Beyond that, a grey cloud sits on the empty land'?

V

DEADS' TOWN NEEDS SOAP

*A person has to be dead before he can know
how good it is to be alive.*

THERE ARE two things I want to say as plainly and honestly as I can before I tell you what I learned on this journey. First, there was nothing intrepid about going. If I had needed to conquer any fear, or failing that, to have carried my qualms with me, there might have been a measure of valour in the undertaking. In the past two years, I had walked for many sundowns over jungle trails and I had seen many sun-ups from the doorways of native huts. Always, I had been shown only courtesy and hospitality. From my carriers, I had known perfect co-operation. Some of the men must have been older than I (they seldom have any idea of their own age), but they called me Ma, and I felt that relationship toward them.

The carrying-men may have seemed brutish, extravagantly vengeful, under my house while they devised imaginative tortures for a man they abhorred, but as long as they spit out their anger in loud voices which I could plainly hear, he was in no danger. Had a tribesman behaved in the manner in which the man they called Ants habitually conducted himself, a lethal portion of crocodile gall would have been stirred into his pepper soup. The nearest Ants ever came to being poisoned was by his own hand when he bought a quantity of distilled cane-juice one night after his supply of bottled liquor ran out. Had Ants wished to cross the country on a bush trip, the only white with a company of men like my carriers, he could have done so and been safe from harm – though not from every frustration and inconvenience which they could have contrived to seem accidental.

The other thing that I want to say is that there was nothing noble about this undertaking. Baysah was right when he said that I really wanted to go and that otherwise, I would not have gone. I would have been disappointed if he had told me what he knew about Comma back there in his store.

It is hard to explain exactly what is the powerful allurement of jungle trails and hinterland villages. I know that whenever I have been in foreign places where there has been an effort to transplant intact a slice of westernized living, something dismal hangs over the place, a pall of ennui. The graft never quite takes. Days lack purpose, go limp. After sundown life is crisped up with rounds of iced drinks, only to wilt again when sunrise presages another hot and useless day. It is partly to get back a robust appetite for life that one goes to live among the native people, who devour each small incident of the day, happy or otherwise, with healthy zest. Often when you start out over an unmarked, unmapped trail, you do not care where it goes or the names of the villages along the way, because the place where you are really hoping to go is toward a better understanding of yourself.

Most travellers through the deep forests of tropical Africa have experienced a sense of pilgrimage. The reason for the trip and the excuse for going are often quite different.

Graham Greene, writing about his trek through Liberia (*Journey without Maps*), said, 'Africa, not a particular place, but a shape, a strangeness, a wanting to know . . . the shape, of course, is roughly that of the human heart.'

When the farthest foot of road ends against a wall of forest and the path goes under your feet, winding between the trees as insignificantly as a mouse runs under a field of grain, there is hope that under the massive boughs, under the litter of ancient decaying wood and layers of fallen leaves, you will find the archetypal mould in which you first were cast. As you live in the villages under the brim of the forest, you become contemporary with the people who have lived in shelters of mud and thatch for centuries, and you get the feeling that this is where you started from many generations ago. You have come the long way back, you have come home. Then you begin to understand truths that you would not know if you had not travelled the long distance away, and what seems the shorter trip, the distance back.

Comma, then, was my excuse for going; I was my own reason.

After we were beyond sight of Baysah's shop, Zabogi tried to spur us to a faster pace. He would rush to the head of the caravan and back again whenever there was space for him to pass, barking, 'Make go! Make go!' If a frog could walk upright on its hind legs, the silhouette would roughly caricature Zabogi – the enormous chest, the thick throat, the protruding eyes, the skinny legs bent above spread feet. When Zabogi moved, his big loose belly did a side-slap; the whole great bulk of his frame wambled sideways in rebellion against the command of his mind to get into energetic forward motion. Since I was in the lead, no one could walk faster than I, so I assumed his frenzied activity was directed toward accelerating my pace and I tried to comply.

When I turned my head in the direction of his retreating figure, I could see out of the tail of my eye that he would pause a moment abreast Tama as though searching for fault.

Before she stepped off Baysah's piazza and slipped into line just ahead of Comma, Tama had pulled her new gold *lappa* tight to stretching over her hip-beads. Every ripple of muscle in her neat little buttocks was accentuated by the wet cloth clinging to her like a second brighter pelt. Her plum-purple

C*

skin, spangled with raindrops, glistened above the gold cloth. Tama invested all her movements with a delicate flutter; there seemed a sort of kinship between her bright beauty and the clouds of butterflies that flitted around our feet. Her eyes had an expression of studied demureness as befitted a wife being taken home for a beating, but that expression only veiled something else which glinted through. I was rather sure that the something else was the *frisky* she had promised to leave behind, and had not.

Zabogi would have changed her position in the procession, I believe, if he could have thought of any subtle way to do it. Had he simply ordered her back with him, every man in the line would have understood the reason and guffawed inwardly unless he dared to laugh aloud. Tama definitely was not walking like a man!

We paused for the first time when we achieved the crest of a series of hilly rises of land. The path detoured here around a heap of leaves and sticks higher than our heads.

'Wait, all!' Zabogi ordered. Everyone set down his load and watched Zabogi as he came slowly past them toward the green heap, a twig in his hand. He bowed to the mound and then pressed the twig rapidly to the outside of his right knee, the inside of the left, the outside again. This was so swiftly done, it seemed almost sleight-of-hand, as though the twig had passed through his legs like a needle.

'All the bad that is in me, I wish to leave here on the path. May no evil thing hide in me and stay inside. Even the bad I do not know, I leave here.' He was solemn-faced as he cast the twig on the pile. 'I go ahead now, clean.'

One by one the carriers, came forward and did the same, reverently as communicants approaching an altar. They approached it with bent posture, walking heavily, but as soon as each had placed his twig on the mound, he straightened his back as though shed of a burden. Some of them even shook themselves like a dog just out of a bath. Most of them moved their lips as though in silent prayer. 'Telling their bads,' Johnny whispered to me.

Comma and Tama hung back. 'I must carry my bads,' Tama apologized to the pile. 'I am not free to leave them here.' Then she looked at Zabogi and her nostrils flared slightly with a suggestion of contempt. 'Zabogi would have no reason to beat me before my people if I left my bads here.' She giggled prettily then, looking at all the men. Her arms were crossed over her impudent little breasts and she gave herself a tiny hug. Tama treasured her sins, was delighted that she had an excuse to keep them a little longer.

Comma came forward then and made his explanation to the depository. 'It is for the sasswood to say whether I carry a big bad in me. If I have thieved, that is too big a bad to wrap in a leaf and leave beside the trail. Only fire will make it clean.'

Johnny cupped his lips to my ear. 'Do like the others,' he whispered. 'Else the Lomas will think you are too proud to admit any bad.' He pressed a twig into my hand.

'Shall I name the bad thing I wish to leave here?' I asked them.

'If you wish, Ma.' Zabogi nodded. 'Your words will tie it down.'

'All right, then. My wish is that I could wrap and leave here all the bad things that make trouble between people whose skin is different-different colour.'

They did not say anything at all, but their pleasure was in their faces as, one by one, they filed past me and pressed both their palms to mine as they went back to pick up their loads.

The rain had slackened. As we started on again, the wind was soughing through the top of the forest, making sad, great music above the columns and arches of the trees. When the sun finally shone, the light filtered through to us in oblique shafts. Every leaf was water-glossed and clean; the damp air washing across our faces was rain-fresh. In a mood of quiet elation, I walked ahead for hours.

The path was well marked and uncluttered. Tree-trunks lying across the trail had passage-ways hacked through them. None of the streams was wide or deep enough to cause any long delay. I crossed them sitting on Zabogi's powerful shoulders, clutching his hair with one hand, clamping his jutting chin with the other.

By mid-afternoon it was apparent to Zabogi that we were not going to reach Sanoyea before dark, in spite of our good pace. (I had delayed too long at Baysah's place). We would have walked on into the night, he said, except that there was a river ahead too dangerous to cross after dark. He was deeply troubled.

A tribesman is drenched with terror at even the mention of spending a night in the jungle. It is not wild animals he fears; a fire will stand off man's natural enemies. Things neither animal nor human, and too dreadful to mention, crawl and creep and fly through the forest at night. The darkness pulsates with sinister beings. A man can swallow a demon with a gulp of air. The nostril hairs will not strain out little gnomes no bigger than a gnat which buzz in the head until the brain is gone.

'This river ahead, Zabogi? Is it wide?'

He shook his head.

'Is it deep, then?'

'Not more deep than one man standing on another man's head, even when it is full. Small swift, yes. But in the daylight, it is nothing of a river.'

'If I were not along, would you go on and try for Sanoyea tonight?'

He shook his head wildly. 'No, Ma, I fear that river for my own self, It is near Deads' Town. At night, the dead come to the river to wash away the dirt of the grave and make themselves clean.'

'Did you ever see them?'

'I feared to look, Ma. But I have heard them. You can hear them slapping their grave clothes on the rocks to beat them clean. There is an old man in Sanoyea who has seen them, though. He is blind. He spied on the dead while they were bathing and he never saw anything after that.'

'You must do what you and the others wish,' I said. 'But if you want to go on through, I will tell you how we can manage. When we are near the river, you can call out in a big voice and tell the dead people that we are coming. Tell them that if they will go away until we pass, we will leave them some sweet-soap on the bank for their washing. I will cross first; you do not need to carry me. We will tie the electric torch on the top of my head, and when I have swum across, I will turn the light back over the water. Then you can all follow the light the the place where I stand.'

He considered this. 'You won't fear, Ma?'

'No fear,' I lied. 'I would rather get wet in the river than to sleep all night on the wet ground.'

That was true. There is a Lutheran Mission in Sanoyea, and the thought of a clean bed dwarfed all the obstacles between me and it.

'Suppose the dead have not all left when we get to the river? We would all turn blind.' Zabogi was not quite ready to agree to my plan.

'We can listen. If they are there, we will hear them beating on the rocks, not so?'

Perhaps if I could get some conversation going at the critical moment, it would muffle the sound.

'All right,' Zabogi said, 'if you will go first. I would rather try to cross than to try to sleep on the path. But, Ma, how shall I manage to take you back to the plantation if you are blind?'

'I will not put my eye on anything that a person should not see,' I promised him.

He took word of the plan back along the line of the carriers. They discussed it one way and another. To sleep on the trail was terrible; to risk disturbing the dead was terrible. The choice was a grim one between two terribles. They spoke of awful things that had happened to men who had slept in the forest.

Latoka knew a man who had been caught out alone at night. The man had put his back against a big bombox tree. The buttress roots of the tree were higher than the man's head, even when he was standing. They enclosed him all around except in front, where he had a fire. The man felt safe enough to doze fitfully. Also in the forest that night was the spirit of a new-dead who had been so evil in his life that he feared to go to God's Town. The spirit saw the fire of the sleeper and came toward it to get warm.

Since this dead man had been so wicked and had spoiled so many of God's plans for good things in his village, his neighbours had not given his spirit a funeral feast. A departed spirit has to sit on a log and shiver or wander forlornly about in the night-chill until the feast has been made, so this spirit was extremely cold. The fire looked better to him than anything he had seen in his whole life. When the spirit saw the man behind the fire, all relaxed, the warm life-blood beating in his temples, the warm breath coming out of his mouth, he was so jealous from wanting to be alive that he seized the man and threw him into the fire, thinking to take his place against the tree, a living being. The man was burned all over. Latoka had seen his drawn skin where the fire had eaten him. The place where the spirit's bony fingers had clutched the man's neck had made a wound that never healed. Latoka had seen it and the way it was shaped like fingers.

All the carriers knew and related similar incidents, and no one disputed the truth of any of the tales. By the time dark fell, the cumulative effect was a frenzy of fear.

We had kerosene lanterns which we lighted and placed at

intervals with the men. These cast our shadows into gargoyle monsters, lure to the menacing spirits which surrounded us because a man's shadow 'makes a handle' by which a demon can lift him up and bear him away. But even with the distorting shadows, the lanterns were better than the murk of the night. Talking was given up entirely. We moved stealthily, our footfalls muffled by the moss on the path. It was so quiet I could hear Johnny's breath behind me, coming and going in nervous rhythm, a faint snort and a tiny wheeze. Also, I could hear my own heart pounding in my ears. It sounded like a drum gone mad.

I tried to reason myself into calm. Their demons and shades and goblins and monsters were not mine. I had often hunted in the forests near the plantation at night and it had always seemed a lark. I walked now with a .45 revolver strapped to my hip and a good rifle in my arm. I was not afraid to meet wild game. What, then, was left to fear?

A whiff of strong acrid odour, a sweetish putrefaction, stung my nostrils. It clung to me like something foul on the sole of a shoe; I could not pass through it. The men had often insisted that fear has its own unmistakable odour, and that they can always smell fear in another person, or even in themselves. I thought this was a figure of speech, using 'smell' to mean 'sense' or 'intuition.' They made it clear that it was not, and they were astonished that I had never experienced or identified fear-smell. They considered this a sense of defect in a class with partial blindness. 'When a man fears a dog,' they said, 'the dog smells the man's fear-stink and it hurts his nose. That is why a dog bites a man who fears him. The dog vexes because of the hurt in his nose.' They said, too, that people caught fear from one another like a sickness; it was contagious. I am willing to believe that I smelled human fear that night, and that I caught it. The smell of it is akin to the odour of death.

I have never heard that calmness is a contagion, but I knew

must achieve it for myself, at least, before we reached the
river.

'All right, now! I will concentrate on something else, some
good book I have read.'

So, what do I think of? Walter de la Mare's 'The Wharf'.
I see the empty barge floating on the dark river, the soul-
scooper flailing his shovel at a harpy! – No, no, not de la Mare
tonight! His stories are for a comfortable chair beside a
crackling fire. You can afford to let your mind wander into
other-worldliness when your body is settled on familiar
cushions. No de la Mare nor Poe. Oh, so now I have to think
of Poe! And be unable to stop thinking of him until memory
has whirled through all his stories of the macabre!

On and on, over miles of trail, I could not get my mind to
settle on a single comfortable bit of literature. If only I could
have remembered some dull treatise on government, a bulletin
on gardening, or a comfortable quote from the Upanishads!
Shakespeare was no good. All I could visualize were the shades
in Macbeth. The Bible? I saw Saul, after he had banished
wizards and diviners out of the land, going on a gloomy night
such as this, forsaken by God, disguised in old clothes (country
cloth?), a supplicant, to the cave of the witch of Endor. The
angry ghost of Samuel towers over Saul and he cowers.

'Listen, Ma, do you hear them?' The bulk beside me was
Zabogi, whispering.

I started. I was still in the first book of Samuel. The Philis-
tines were swarming over the battlefield at Gilboa to strip
the slain, and had just come upon Saul and his 'three sons
fallen.'

'Hear what?'

'Why, the dead. Who else?'

I listened. I heard the faint rush of distant water.

'Is it time to call out to them?' I whispered.

'Not yet, but soon now. I will walk back of you and tell
you when it is time to lift your voice.'

'It is your voice that is going to get lifted,' I reminded him. 'Remember?'

'I don' think I got any voice.' His big bulk was shaking as though in the clamp of a malarial chill.

'Well, those Dead don't know English,' I told him. 'You better find your voice.' I didn't want to shatter the stillness with sound any more than he did.

I believe Zabogi put off his warning until what he considered the last possible moment. The sound of water became gradually louder as we approached. There was a slip-slap-slip-slap, and it did sound like a waterside on washday. Also, it sounded like water flowing around an obstruction of boulders. Of course it did. Of course.

. . . And the woman said unto Saul, I saw gods ascending out of the earth. And he said unto her, what form is he of? And she said, An old man cometh up; and he is covered with a mantle. . . .

'I ready now, Ma.' Zabogi gripped my arm with icy fingers. 'I have gathered up my voice.'

'Make it big,' I encouraged him.

Zabogi had gathered up more voice than I knew he had. It blasted our ears like an explosion. When the echo of it came rolling back, I wished that he had not found so much. He went on in spite of that terrible mocking echo, and when he had finished, he told Johnny to find the sweet-soap he had promised *them* that he would leave on the far bank.

While Johnny rummaged for the soap, Zabogi lashed the flashlight to my head. The weight of it bent over the top of my right ear but he wouldn't readjust it.

'No mind for one ear,' he croaked. 'It will stop hurting when we take the light off.'

I tried to keep talking now and to get the others to talk in order to cover that slip-slap-slip.

'All right now, Ma,' Zabogi said. 'Gun off! And out of your heavy trouser. I will put my eye away from you if you feel shame, and I will wear your trouser over on my head,

all dry for you, when I follow. Keep your shoes on until we stand on the bank. It is only around a curve, now.'

My knees clacked together and so did my teeth as I undressed.

'Terrible damn-cold hellova night, Ma.' Zabogi was trying to be game but he was chattering too. I agreed with his estimate.

'It's so cold I am sweating.' I told him, and he managed a feeble laugh. I stood there on the bank in my underwear, clutching him, while I turned my head from side to side to sweep the river with the flashlight.

The water looked like oil, its movement scarcely noticeable. Something white floated slowly past.

'Whoooo,' Zabogi shuddered. 'One of the Deads left too fast and lost his grave-clothes.'

. . . *An old man cometh up; and he is covered with a mantle.* . . .

'Let Johnny find a length of cloth in the dash-chest,' Zabogi begged. 'We will leave it with the soap. Poor old naked Dead!'

'OK. Sure,' I said. Then I plunged in. If I had waited another minute, I would have been too panic-stricken to do it at all.

It was, as Zabogi had said, a nothing of a river. I had to swim for only a few strokes. The rest was wading depth. The current was not swift and the far bank was an easy scramble.

I released my bent ear, and made a path of light for the others to follow. Tama came first. Midway across, she shrieked and went under. I kept the light on the place, so I did not see who jumped in next, or next, but it was the wizened little Latoka who dragged her out.

'Oh, *they* caught at my legs! *They* pulled me under!' She was blubbering and screaming. 'Deads' Town wants me!'

'Shut up!' I said. 'Do you want the others to cross or do

you want them to run all the way back to Salala and leave us here alone?'

Tama didn't even hear me but Latoka did. He smacked her across the mouth so hard that she plumped down in the wet clay.

'Comma is still in there, Ma,' Latoka said, 'I go fetch him now.'

Latoka found Comma washed up against a tree root, con-siderably downstream. He was limp but alive. As I kneeled astride Comma and tried to remember the mechanics of artificial respiration, Zabogi, in good voice, was shouting the necessary orders from the far bank, getting the loads over one by one. Latoka went back to help him. Apparently, they were confident that I had not run into the dreaded rightful inhabitants of the place. Tama kept on blubbering.

'Make go! Make go!' I heard Zabogi shout. 'The Deads can't stay away all night for we to pass.'

When Zabogi was finally across, he took a look at Comma. 'Stand aside, Ma. Let me doctor him.'

Zabogi hauled back one of his enormous feet, and putting all his weight behind the swing, kicked Comma in the seat. Comma flailed one arm, rolled on his side, and vomited an amazing quantity of muddy water.

'Is that how you doctor drowned people?' I asked him.

'That's how I doctor lazy carriers,' he said. 'Comma set his load down when he went in after Tama, and I had to bring that damn-heavy money case over on my own head.'

'Let's put this place behind us,' Johnny said. 'I will stand under the money case.'

'Make go! Make go!' Zabogi ordered. 'This waterside don't belong to we.'

Comma was sitting up now, blinking wretchedly at the lanterns. Zabogi plopped the roosters on Tama's head, and when she objected, he swatted her bottom with the flat of his hand. Comma, seeing the others leaving, staggered to his feet and wobbled after them. It was the duty of Zabogi and myself to be the last to leave the outskirts of Deads' Town.

'I don't smell fear any more, Zabogi,' I told him in an almost normal voice.

'Oh, so now you know the smell of fear,' he said admiringly. 'Well, a place like that makes a person come alive.'

'How far now, to Sanoyea?'

'Ma,' he said, 'there is a something I have got to tell you. We can't go through after all. My great toe hangs down. I think I broke it against Comma's behind. We will have to sleep in the bush, after all.'

'Shall we sleep here then?'

'Oh, no!' He shook his head wildly. 'I can manage to walk until the river is not in our ears any more. Then we will watch for a big old bombox tree, and we will sleep there with the roots around all of us, and the fire in front.'

We found a suitable tree, finally. Building a fire took a long time. Latoka whittled the wet bark off dead sticks with his cutlass and splintered the centres. We used a few precious drops of kerosene out of one of the lanterns, and after a lot of smoke and splutter, we had light and heat. The men didn't want to cook, hungry though they were, so we opened some tins of corned beef and portioned out the cold meat.

'Now,' I said, 'we will sleep close together. That way we can have more blankets under us and over us.'

The tree-roots formed a big encircling cove on the leeward side, coming almost together again in the space where we had the fire. It was like a circular hut without any roof, except for the leaves far above us.

'I will sleep on the outside toward the forest,' I said. 'I will have the gun beside me, and the man who stands the watch can sit by my feet and call me if we need the gun.'

'It is my rightful place to sleep beside the Mommio,'

ohnny announced. 'When we are on the trail I always sleep
across her feet [across the doorway of a hut]. I guard her.'

'Haw-haw, tee-hee!' Latoka jeered. 'You guard her! My
mother had some small chickens. When a big bird came to
get them, one chicken found his way into the rice hamper
and ate my Ma's rice. When she found him there, he said,
"Look I am guarding your rice from the big bad bird in the
bush."'

'You will stand the first watch, that's what you'll do,'
Zabogi said to Johnny.

'Ma,' Tama was still sobbing, 'they want me in Deads'
Town. Let me hang on to you tonight so *they* can't carry
me. I beg you, Ma.'

Zabogi was disgusted with her. 'They don't want you,
Tama. The Deads are nice quiet people. They wouldn't have
you.'

Comma spoke then for the first time since his ducking.
His voice sounded water-logged.

'Maybe they wanted your new gold *lappa*, Tama. Maybe
that is why they pulled at your leg.'

She was enormously comforted. 'Sure, they would want
it. In the morning, I will go back and leave it on the bank
for them. I will make sacrifice of my fine gold *lappa* and then
the Deads will leave me be. Only tonight, I must hang tight
to the Ma.'

Johnny seemed to think it had been an extravagant crossing. 'First, Deads' Town needs soap,' he said. 'After, one old
naked Dead loses his grave-clothes and we have got to leave
a fine American cloth for him. Now it is Tama's new *lappa*
that cost Zabogi plenty days' pay. Those Deads must have
studied to bargain under Baysah.'

'Let's keep our tongues down,' I said. 'I'm tired.'

'Oh, Ma,' Latoka said, 'you can sleep, but sleep can't sit
on any we in this place.'

Tama clung to me with arms like steel bands around my

chest. If the angel of death had come for her in the night h
couldn't have wedged his scythe between us to pry her away

When I awakened the next morning, Johnny was sprawle
forward, his head wedged against the soles of my feet. H
was in the guard's spot, so I knew he had fallen asleep ther
and never been replaced by a second watchman. I proppe
myself up on one elbow and wriggled my toes in his hair
He yawned and blinked and we grinned at each other.

'You're a fine watchman,' I teased him.

'I'm a better steward,' he admitted. 'I go now, make u
the fire, make coffee, before these others wake up. Then
will tell them how Johnny, the brave Bassau, watched ove
the sleeping Lomas the whole night and kept the fire big!'

VI

THE TELLS AND THE TOLDS

A man cannot have his house in two towns.

ONE BY ONE the sleepers roused, sat up wordlessly, yawned and stretched. They fumbled their way to the sputtering fire where Johnny was roasting yams for our breakfast. He allotted each man a portion of the coffee-grounds left from the bitter brew I was drinking. Johnny's coffee was as dark as his skin but the men thought it anaemic stimulant; dregs had the only concentration worth bothering to carry to the mouth. They sat on their haunches, big-eyed, relaxed of face after their heavy slumber. The dew shone like pearls in the kinks of their hair.

'Sleep never sat on me the whole night,' Zabogi grumbled. 'My toe hurt me. See how big it has grown.'

'I never saw it small!' – stonily from Tama.

Johnny studied Zabogi's face, all drooped with sleep. 'Oh, Zabogi,' he chanced, 'then you can witness, since you never shut your eye the whole night, how I stood guard, and kept the fire big, and never called another watchman.'

'So you did, Johnny,' Zabogi confirmed. The glances they exchanged established confederacy between two accomplished liars.

'I had a terrible bad dream,' the carrier Dika said. 'Dika' means 'spark,' an allusion to his hair which was startlingly red. Dika knew his appearance was absurd and he had moulded his personality to fit. Dika was our clown and fool.

'Oh? Dika?' Zabogi asked politely.

The only way to keep a nightmare from becoming a reality is to tell it. Dika must be allowed to destroy the evil of the night with his tongue.

'Yes, man,' Dika said. 'I dreamed that all the BADS that are in that pile of leaves back there on the path got a big stir from the wind; the wind turned them all loose on one village.'

'Ooooh,' they shivered, each remembering the sins he had contributed, perhaps. 'What then, Dika? What happened?'

'Oh, it was a palaver, I tell you! But I can't tell you all of it. If I told you, too plenty women would get beat. No bush would get cut to make farm; the men would be that busy beating their wives. The people would starve because no farm would be brushed. That is how many BADS women have put there!'

'The people would starve for true,' Tama agreed archly. 'The reason is that all the mens would be *dead* if women knew how many BADS that *men* have left there!'

Tama was especially beautiful when she was vexed. The heat of her anger seemed to glow through her skin and her big eyes shone with animal-gleam. The arts of the poison-pot are one of the crafts girls learn in the Sande, their tribal secret school in the bush. No harm in reminding the men of it on suitable occasions! The knowledge is seldom used by tribeswomen. It is not necessary to wield this power for the simple reason that men know their wives possess it.

'Oh, I had a worse dream than that,' Latoka bragged. (It was clearly time to change the subject.) 'I sneaked on my belly until I lay right under an elephant.'

Latoka was a shrivelled little fellow with an always-hungry look, and shoulders no wider than an elephant's hoof.

'I lay there still, still; in my hand the spear that has a hook on the end. I raised the spear slow, slow. All right! Just as I gathered all my strength to push the spear deep into his middle, old elephant took a lazy step and put his foot right down on me. This pushed me down into the wet ground. I

felt no hurt, only the heaviness of the elephant, but no hurt. When I got up I was pressed thin as a leaf. I was so thin the wind tore me at the edges, and I rattled like a banana stalk. I heard Old Wind give easy-friend laugh. When I started to walk, I knew the reason. I had no need to use my feet! Old Wind made himself flat against my back and pushed. I was just above the ground and never touched it. Where trees had fallen, Old Wind just lifted me up easy and over. Oh, it was fine until we came to the village where we were to sleep!'

'What then, Latoka? What was not fine?' Zabogi was nursing his broken toe, thinking probably how fine it would be to keep that big spud of misery skimming just above the path, never touching rocks.

'Oh, it was bad in the village,' Latoka assured us. 'All the women pointed their fingers at me and made tee-hee. So, I am glad to have my own shape, awkward as it is, back on my bones this morning. When the rocks hurt my feet, I will not vex. I learned sense from my bad dream.'

'Bad! Bad, for true.' They all knew that it takes less courage to rip the insides out of a live elephant than to face a woman's tee-hee. But a whole village of women! And all making tee-hee! Bad, bad!

While the others sported their dreams Comma sat a little apart huddled under a blanket, his arms clasped around his raised, shivering knees. The incubus of his own personal night-terror still sat upon him, weighting his head down to his chest.

Tama was the only one who took notice. 'Comma?'

He seemed not to hear her, nor to have been listening to any of us. She rose and went to him, shook him gently.

'What bad thing lay on you in the night, Comma? Tell it out so it will be gone from you.'

His effort of speech loosened a racking cough. 'I was putting the marks of my learning on my arm,' he said, turning his wrist so we could all see the row of commas.

'Why my dream-self needed to do this, I cannot say, since the marks are there already. In my dream, I took cotton from my mother's farm and soaked it a long time in palm oil, just as I did when I marked myself long ago. Then I made the cotton into round pads as big as ha'p'nies, and laid them out in a row on my skin. Next, I twisted the little stems to put on the round parts. I was ready then to take a stick out of the cooking-fire and light the cotton so it would burn me deep and fine, and the marks would be plain.

'But in my dream, when I reached for the fire, something pulled my arm away. I looked and saw that it was Ka Nyene [a forest monster who will help people but in return must be given whatever he asks]. Ka Nyene said, "Give me the cotton! I want to suck the palm oil out of it." So, I had to give it to Ka Nyene, and my arm remained smooth and I had no marks. Ka Nyene had terrible red eyes and his spit was green as a leaf, and ran out of the corners of his mouth down on the long black hair of his chest.'

The men nodded. Latoka knew a man who had met Ka Nyene, and he had described the monster the same way.

'Ka Nyene swallowed my cotton,' Comma went on sadly. 'Then he belched. The sound was like thunder. Civilized marks would not lie down easy in his belly. He said, "You belong to me now, Comma. Learning cannot hold you!" '

Comma felt his raised scars as though to satisfy himself they were still there, that they had not been plucked off him like pennies in the night.

'My marks are not so bright as always before. Do you think so, Mommio?'

'Wait until the sun is higher and shines on them,' I told him. 'I see no change.'

When Comma had burned the marks into his skin he had rubbed indigo under the blister. They were bright as bluing.

'I fear they will fade away, Mommio.' Tears brimmed on his lashes.

'No mind, Comma.' Zabogi was showing rare good will toward the boy. 'Now put this into your head: the tooth-marks of the Devil [scars made ritually in the Poro or Devil's Bush] never fade.'

The others nodded, all but Johnny. The Devil had never 'eaten' Johnny.

'I dreamed I had a new *pickin*,' Tama said. 'And when it made the first sound, it did not cry.'

Zabogi was instantly the solicitous father. 'Oh, Tama, it laughed? A bad dream for true.'

If a baby laughs before it cries, it is considered unnatural; it 'has witch'. When God was busy making the earth, his grandchild annoyed him by crying in heaven. God said, 'Crying has got to go down out of here. I can't do my work proper.' So, God sent crying down to earth to get it out of heaven; he did not send laughter down until the hard work was all finished.

'Oh, the baby did something worse than laugh,' Tama tittered. 'It bellowed like a bush-cow bull.' She gave an unbullish bellow, and the men's deep voices corrected her until everyone but Comma and the 'new father' were delightedly roaring like an enraged buffalo.

'But, that is not all!' Tama clapped them to attention. 'When the Sade Ki [midwife] saw it, she said "EEeeee! It is not a *pickin* Tama has had. An animal came out of her!' Then she accused me – said I had slept in the bush with an animal. The child had rough skin with spots on it and wide feet with webs between. When the Sade Ki showed it to the people they were all ready to accuse me of being frisky with an animal. But then, they saw it had eyes out of its head like a frog. They knew by that Zabogi was the true father and that I had not slept with an animal, but only with my husband, as a good woman should.'

The men pointed their fingers at Zabogi and yelped their glee. He bulged his big tobacco-brown eyes and looked more

roggish than ever. He was grinning over the answer he was
bout to make before the men could stifle their guffaws and
ettle down to listen.

'I also dreamed you had new *pickin*, Tama. Not one, but
lenty, plenty. They got borned out of your mouth. The
ame of all the *pickin* was the same. The name was Foolish.
All the little Foolish were empty and had no weight, so Old
Wind took them away. By the time he got to the far country,
Old Wind saw they were no use, so he let them down out
f his arms in a heap. They dried up in the sun and each one
vas a kernel of sand. That is how got made the Land-of-the-
ig-sand [the Sahara]. God never made the Land-of-the-big-
and. The woman, Tama, made it with all the small Foolish
hat got borned out of her big ol' mouth.'

The men were wide awake now, ready for the trail. Stagger-
ng with laughter, they began to get under their loads. None
f the evil they had dreamed could happen. It had been fore-
talled by the telling. If any of them had dreamed a good
hing, the rest of us would never know it because telling will
lso prevent pleasant things from happening. When a dream
valks, it can blunder into dark and terrible places and still
eep its feet, but when the dreamer wakes a spoken word is
irge enough to trip it!

'Take your loads and get you on the path,' Zabogi ordered
hem. 'I will follow as soon as Latoka has fixed my broken
oe.'

'Oh,' Tama wailed. 'I lacked small to forget a big some-
hing! I have got to make sacrifice of my new gold *lappa*. I
nust carry it back to the river and leave it there for the Deads.'

'I will go with you, Tama, and guard you,' Comma volun-
ered. He had lingered behind the others to smother another
ege of coughing.

'You will go on down the trail, Comma, and save your
et-down lungs,' Zabogi told him. 'Tama can go alone. The
eads sleep by day.'

'All right,' Comma agreed finally with a wheeze. 'On the path; you are the chief, so *for now* I have got to do as you say. If you like, I will doctor your toe before I leave; tomorrow I am a doctor.'

'Today,' Zabogi told him, 'you are a fool. Everyday i. today. Tomorrow is never. Get the path under you.'

'I wonder if the Deads would agree for my almost new *lappa*?' Tama mused. 'It is not spoiled in any part. I want to wear my new gold one when I stand up to be beat.'

'Remember, you got to pass this waterside again when we come back,' Latoka counselled. 'The Deads got nothing much to do but remember things people promise them.'

'Maybe I won't come back,' Tama threatened, giving her torso a saucy fling. 'Maybe I will stay with my people.'

'Don't humbug me when my toe hurts, woman!' Zagob was peevish. 'Your people have not got the bride-price to turn back to me. They will talk sense to you, tell you what a fine man has got you.'

'Maybe they spent the bride-price they took from you,' Tama retorted, 'but I got a sister. They could give you m' sister.'

'Tie your mouth, woman!' Zabogi turned full attention to his toe which Latoka was binding with some splints of palm mid-rib.

'I want to keep that gold *lappa*.' Tama was rummaging for her almost-best. It was an indigo *batik*, superior beyon compare to the sleazy imported rayon she treasured. I ha been coverting that *batik* for a long time.

'Leave the gold one on the river-bank, Tama,' I said. 'When we get back to the plantation, I will buy you anothe just like it, and a head-cloth besides, if you will let me hav the blue one.'

'Oh, Ma,' she said, 'you don't want the blue one. It is country thing. It don't shine.'

'I do want it! So, let the Deads have the gold one.'

'All right.' She was still reluctant, though. 'But, Ma, the Deads have got sense for cloth past you.' She wrapped herself in the country thing that didn't shine and started back toward the river with the gold one in a crumpled bundle on her head.

Comma, still dallying with his load, watched her out of sight, his big almond-eyes clouded with wistfulness. Then he started down the trail in the opposite direction.

Latoka whacked out a crude wooden sandal, roughly the shape of a catcher's mitt, and bound it to Zabogi's foot. Then he took one of the spent fowls Tama had been carrying and talked to it a long time in Loma. Suddenly then, he broke one of its toes, snapping it like a twig.

'No, Latoka!' I was angry. 'You can't do that!'

'Sure I can, Ma. I already did it.' Triumphant puckish grin. The rooster's toe was bandaged just like Zabogi's. 'When the chicken's toe don't hang down when we take off the sticks, then we can take the sticks off Zabogi's toe. Don't white people know that one, Ma?'

'Look, Ma!' Zabogi pointed out to the path where rain was flooding down. 'See there it rains, but here where we are, no rain falls. And all the whole night, no rain fell on we.'

Freak storms like that are common in the tropics; sometimes the line between wet and dry is astonishingly demarked.

'Why do you think it is so, Zabogi?'

'Oh, God saw us down here with no roof for head, Ma. All God had to do was hold one hand over us and let the rain fall off the edges all around us. The hand of God is big enough to cover all we.'

I studied him closely to see how literally he meant this. He looked back at me, solemn, unblinking.

'Who told you what you know of God, Zabogi?'

'Told?' he repeated. 'Told? Whoever is so stupid that they got to be *told* about God? Never did any man know God from *tolds*. You get God by *feels*. All the told there is to it, is his name. You call him God; we call him Gala. I English

Gala's name so you can understand me. Come on, Ma. Let go!'

'What about Tama?'

'She will catch us. After she lays her *lappa* by the river she will run this way like all the Deads wanted her to carry them to Lomaland on her head.'

'Maybe,' I ventured, 'if you would show more take-care for Tama, you would not have so much palaver with her.'

'More take-care?' Zabogi's jaw was agape with amazement. 'I show enough take-care to walk seven sundowns to beat her, and you want I should show more take-care past that? I sure glad I not married to a white woman.'

'You'd get your bride-price back in a hurry if you treated one the way you treat Tama.' His stodgy male stubbornness riled me. 'Only thing, white people don't have bride-price.'

'Hmmmn!' He had to chew over the strange lack of that custom. It posed several problems to him. 'What do you call it, Ma, when white woman leaves her husband, and won't never agree to go back to him?'

'Divorce is the word. That, is when they carry it to court and the judge tells them they are finished with being married.'

'There you are with the TELLS and the TOLDS again, Ma! He was as impatient with my views as I was with his. 'I don't need no TOLDS to know that I am married. Married palaver is like God-palaver; you know it by feels out of your heart not tolds out of another person's mouth. Now, Ma, tell me how white people manage about the vexes. No persons can live together without they have vexes, sometimes. How is it that all white people don't get divorce if there is no matter of bride-price to hold them together until the small hot vexes get cold?'

'Quite a few white people do get divorces,' I admitted.

'What I don't see is how any of them stay married,' Zabogi said. 'White men ought to have to pay bride-price! It don't show proper respect for a woman to take her for free.'

'Now in regard to Tama,' I persisted. 'You showed her respect when you paid the big dowry. You tell me you show take-care when you walk a far ways to beat her. But now, Zabogi, I want to throw you some sense about women! Women like the small take-care, every day, every day.'

'Like what, Ma?'

'Oh, like you tell Tama how fine she looks.'

'Tama knows that one. It is too big in her head already.'

'Well then, like you help her carry water from the waterside. Or you fetch some firewood for the cooking fire. Small things.'

'Oh, hell, Ma!' Zabogi couldn't muffle his utter disgust. 'You are a woman, Ma, but you don't know one whole damn thing about womens. I will tell you, who ought to know by being one, what a woman likes. A *woman likes to be chiefed!*'

I was only reinforcing convictions he firmly held, so I kept still. Besides, I had a slight conviction he might be right. Partly right, anyway!

'Tama will be all right when she gets some more years,' he said confidently. 'Tama will be fine old mamma. The matter with Tama is that the *Zo* did not do good finish-work on her in the bush. The *Zo* didn't cut all of the frisky out of Tama, so Time has got to finish the undone work of the *Zo*.'

The *Zo* is the head woman in the Sande, the secret cult school for adolescent girls. It corresponds to the Poro for the boys. Part of the *Zo's* work is to excise the clitoris and labia minora of each initiate. The operation is performed with a native iron razor after the girls have bathed in the coldest water available to partially numb the pain. One of the reasons given for this surgery is that afterwards a woman has 'heart hunger' only for her husband; 'body-hunger' has been taken from her.

'You do not feed Tama's heart-hunger, Zabogi. And Time does not take away heart-hunger.'

'Oh, Ma!' He had the determined patience of an adult try-

ing to communicate with a child who is not very bright. '1
is all right for white womens to think on heart-hungers an
swell them big. They do not have much work to do. Blac
women have to work, all the time work, to keep the rice-po
full. There is no strength left to know if the heart is empty
White mens would have a more easy time with their womer
if the womens had to weed rice fields. For true, Ma, I don
see how it is that white people, every one, do not get divorce

'Zabogi,' I said, 'I want to say just one more thing abou
Tama and then I won't talk it any more. Tama is pulle
toward Comma because he touches all things softly. Th
English word for this is gentle. Comma is gentle-handed an
gentle-spoken. His soft words will cage old Town Chief whe
no stick will drive him. Animals and children and wome
like gentle ways, Zabogi. That is what I meant to say when
told you that you should show more take-care for Tam.
I meant you should have gentle ways with her so she woul
not be pulled toward gentle ways in another.'

'Let it lie, Ma,' Zabogi said without rancour. 'Tama won
feel no pull to Comma so soon she finds out she can chi
him. You will see. Anyhow, a man does not take his brother
wife. Our law says we do not do that one.'

'Brother?' I said. 'You and Comma brothers? But you mea
of course, brothers in the way that all Lomas are brothers, o
all Bassaus are brothers.'

'More past that,' Zabogi admitted as though it were
shameful thing to have to say. 'Comma and myself both can
out of our mother, Bola. I was on top [first], of course.'

I could scarcely credit his words. In appearance they e
hibited more differences than might easily be found amor
Loma tribesmen. Comma was the more typical – tall, lon
limbed, agile, oval shapely head, thin features, coppery ski
arrestingly good-looking. Zabogi is the Loma word for ric
hamper. The name fitted his pouch-bellied, broken-bottom
torso, making up in bullish strength and sputtering energ

what it lacked in grace and comeliness. In disposition they were as opposite as in appearance, and in attitude there was deep-rooted hostility instead of the closeness which is notable in hinterland families.

'Your father is a chief, Zabogi. Was Comma's father a slave, that you treat him without brotherness?'

My question was a serious *faux pas*. An African venerates his mother to near-worship. In times of stress, she is his only intermediary with God, his only access to the core of divinity.

Zabogi gave me a withering look. 'Do you think, Ma, that my father, the chief, would give my fine mother to a slave? Bola is fine past all women!'

'I beg you to forget my words,' I said. 'But tell me, who was Comma's father?'

'Comma never had no father. That is what is the matter with him. All his life he has lacked for a father.'

'Everybody has got a father,' I said. 'No one gets born unless he is fathered.'

Zabogi didn't say anything for a long time. Finally, he spoke of his own father.

'My Pa, the chief, is very fine,' Zabogi said. 'The weak in him is that he likes to play gamble. Once, long time since, his luck-medicine went dead, and he had to pawn Bola, my mother, for the play-gamble debts. He tried to get the man to take one of his other wives for a pawn, but the man would have none but Bola. While my mother was in pawn, she borned Comma.'

'Who did Comma belong to then?' I asked. 'Did he belong to your Pa, the chief, or to the man who held Bola and fathered the *pickin*?'

'Our law says that my Pa, the chief, owns Comma, and Comma is his slave. That would be the way of it if the debt had all been paid. Some of it is owing, so Comma does not have to do slave-work for the chief. The man who had Bola and fathered Comma could have bought Comma and had

him for true-son if he had wished. But he wanted no part o
Comma. That is why I told you that Comma never had
father, and that is what is the matter with him.'

'How did Comma get to the Mission, then? Didn't he hav
to serve the chief at all?'

'My Pa didn't want to put eye on him,' Zabogi said
'Every time my Pa put eye on Comma, he thought how hi
weak-part is the play-gamble, and how he had lost Bola, wh
he held high above all women. No one wanted Comma, s
my Ma begged that he be sent to the Mission. Bola said, "I
no man wants this son that has come out of me, then let him
belong to learning."'

'What is he like, Zabogi? The man who got Comm
born?'

'He is a big man,' Zabogi admitted ruefully. 'If he ha
redeemed Comma from my Pa, taken him to his heart fo
true-son, Comma would be bigger man than myself.'

'But your father is the chief, Zabogi. And someday, yo
are to be chief. Who is bigger than a chief, unless it is
paramount chief?'

'The man who got Comma born is the blacksmith,' Zabog
snapped. 'And now, Ma, I don't want to talk any more! Yo
have pressed too plenty TOLDS out of me already.'

Zabogi did not need to tell me any more just then. I alread
knew that the blacksmith is usually the grand master of th
Poro, the Big Devil of the secret cult. The chief of a tow
nominally decides palavers but the Poro master can overrid
any decision a chief may make. No one in the village exce
the Poro initiates know who the Big Devil is, or even that h
is human rather than a spirit. But everyone knows that
blacksmith must be reverenced.

I should say here that although the English word for th
head officials of the Poro is 'Devils', the word carries none
the connotations of 'Satan'. A white man must have bee
responsible, in the beginning, for the appellation, observin

the terror the Poro inspires. Dr. George Way Harley in commenting on the significance of the Poro says, 'The spirits of ancestors are the personification of good. . . . The central figure in the Poro is in the last analysis, a personification of the spirits of the ancestors.' Obviously, 'devil' is not the right word to describe this official, but it is the common term used throughout Liberia, and I use it here for lack of a better one.

Rain pelted my back in innumerable and insufferable tiny thuds. This was not an exhilarating storm, wind-driven and exciting. It was just an exasperating becalmed drizzle.

'The hand of God has got a leak in it,' I complained to Zabogi petulantly, as though it were his fault.

'Yep,' he said, annoyingly cheerful. 'Right between the thumb and first finger. You got to walk faster if you want to stand under God's palm. He can't help if you are too slow.'

Zabogi lurched ahead as though he knew the area of divine shelter to be shifting rapidly in the general direction of the Sahara. I tried to hold the pace he set but could not.

Zabogi had given me a whole fistful of pieces for the jigsaw, and I didn't like the way they seemed to fall into place.

The blacksmith, as head of the Poro, would naturally be alert to sever any connection a tribe-member might have with anti-Poro influences – in this case, the Mission. 'Proving' in the presence of a white that Comma was guilty of theft would certainly seem (to the blacksmith) a logical way to permanently alienate the Mission from Comma. Comma's burns incident to the verdict would be counted small cost. Even though the man was Comma's physical father, he had never accepted Comma as a son. Moreover, in tribal society the group good is always the goal, no matter how many individuals are crushed in achieving it. In *Native African Medicine* Dr. Harley relates that as a part of the sacrifice made to obtain a 'sky-stone' or celt, a *Zo* was required to sacrifice a *favourite* son to obtain the object from his own father, who had obtained it in the same way from his father. It did not seem likely to

me that the blacksmith *Zo* would hesitate for a moment to
allow an *unfavourite* son to be horribly burned for the sake
of perpetuating and strengthening Poro influence in the village.

Even if there were persons in the town who wanted Comma
exonerated, his mother for instance, this influence would
certainly be negligible in the face of whatever the Poro wished.

I had not known that Comma was the rejected son of the
cult head but I would have known if I had thought about it
that the Poro would want to loosen the hold of any modern-
izing influence in their midst, and that the obvious way to
ensure Comma's rejection by this competing power was to
show him unworthy of their concern.

I had consented to witness this trial, convinced that matters
would somehow be arranged to clear the boy. True, I had
worried in the beginning about the burns. But Comma's
confidence and insistence on the trial had reassured me. I was
convinced that Comma had not stolen my money. I thought
that the villagers would also know this, and because of the
fanatical way they abhor theft, would demonstrate for
innocence. I was assuming, of course, that the medicine man
in some way I did not yet understand could control the outcome of the test, that the public ordeal only demonstrated to
a believing audience whatever decision the medicine man had
made, previously and privately.

How could I have failed to see the problem in its large
context – the relation of the Poro with roots in the ancient
past, with laws deriving from the old ones who had died, set
against the new and living threat of Western education?

I had been looking, I realized now, upon this matter simply
as a problem between Comma and his own future. Citizens
of the United States are trained by their own experiences
growing up in a democracy, to consider that an individual
has inalienable rights and privileges and a separate personal
destiny quite apart from that of his associates. We glorify the
Individual, see him in clarity of detail, standing gloriously

separate from the faceless mob through which he moves to achieve according to his abilities. We simply cannot conceive of a way of life in which the mob has the face, the personality, the only possible future, and the individual is an anonymous tiny segment with no life, no soul, no hope, except as he partakes of these as his allotted portion from the aggregate. That is the only excuse I could make for myself for not having seen the situation clearly before I left the plantation.

I knew that I could never live myself out of the horror of what I began to be rather sure was going to happen if that trial took place. I considered turning around right then, going back. I put out a burst of speed in an effort to overtake Zabogi and have it out with him. The carriers, far in front, would have to be overtaken too. Would they consent to turn back? I seriously doubted it. They were joyously headed home. The news had been thudded out ahead of us over the talking drums. That message pulsing from village to village was what kept them going in spite of stone bruises and saw-grass cuts and festering sores on their feet. Going back was the one thing I could not ask of them now unless I was prepared for mutiny.

It seemed doubtful whether I could manage the trip back with only Johnny. The guns were a bigger load than I could carry alone. There would be a necessity for one of the big tins in which we boiled our water. Blankets, food, the heavy money-chest, clothing, would all have to be left behind. Further, I would be breaking a promise to Comma. Turning back was clearly out of the question.

Sick with apprehension, I walked wretchedly on. I could not be sure whether the fever and chills which alternately attacked me came from malaria or a combination of weather and worry. When I wore my big rubber raincoat, I steamed inside it. The smell of the wet rubber mingling with trapped perspiration was horrid. When I took the coat off and carried it, its heavy weight gave me wet slaps and I was immediately

D*

soaked and shaking with cold. Little jets of water dirtied from my mud-caked shoes squirted out of the canvas tops of my shoes with every step. The forest was dimly lighted by the few rays of light that filtered through the leaves which roofed the path. Every forward step seemed to be resisted by an atmosphere as solidly wet and green as though one moved underwater on the ocean floor. I think it must have slowed Zabogi, too. I overtook him, finally.

'Why didn't you tell me before we left the plantation that you and Comma were brothers?' I spoke slowly so he wouldn't notice how short of breath I was.

The face he turned full toward mine was all shiny with rain and homely sincerity 'Why, Ma,' he said, 'you never asked me.'

'Could Comma have gone to the Poro if he had wanted to when the rest of his age-group were initiated?' This was one of the several things I wanted to get straight.

'He could have,' Zabogi said. 'That is where Comma fell in a leopard trap [took the wrong step]. When it was time for all the little mosquitoes [small boys] to become men, the blacksmith 'self asked Comma to leave the school and go to bush.'

'And Comma refused?'

'The Mission refused for him. They told him that if he went to the Poro he could never come back to the Mission.'

'Suppose Comma had gone to the Poro, would the black-smith have taken Comma for his true-son, then?'

'That he would have,' Zabogi said. 'You see, Ma, most babies die soon in our country. The blacksmith told Bola, "I am not going to take your son into my heart until I see if he lives to grow. If he lives through the Poro I will make him mine, for true. Do what you like with him until then. I don't want the Deads to take him and leave a hole in my heart." '

This put the blacksmith in a somewhat better light, I thought, but not much better.

'You see, Ma,' Zabogi went on, 'we do not think a *pickin* is a person until the Devil has eaten him and he is born again out of the Devil's mouth, a man. The Poro Devil swallows mosquitoes and borns them back to the village as men.'

'Do you think Comma wanted to go to the Poro, Zabogi?'

'He sure did want to go, Ma. But he wanted to belong to learning, too. Comma had not yet learned that no man can have his house in two towns. After the Devil's catcher came to the Mission and the Mission refused to let Comma go, he cried all night. The next day his eyes were swelled so he lacked small to see at all; that hard he cried. Then he ran away to our mother's farm and took the cotton and burned the marks of his learning in his skin. All the time he was making those marks, he never cried at all. Some of our people hid and watched him hold his arm quiet while the flame ate his flesh.'

When Tama finally caught up with us, tears mingled with the rain that streaked down her face. I stopped and put my arms around her quivering shoulders.

'What's the matter, Tama? Did you fear back there alone?'

'Oh, no,' she said. 'No fear. It is only that I want to look fine past all women when I stand up to be beat. Now my shine is left for the Deads, who have no need to shine.'

Zabogi clumped on, pausing only to tap his hunky sandal several times on a big rock in order to register in sound his impatience with women.

'Tama, believe me,' I said, 'you would look fine past most women if you had nothing to wear but the old worn-thin blankets that Johnny ties on his feet when he polishes the floor.'

She stopped crying then. 'Ma,' she said, 'if Zabogi would talk sweet-mouth like that to me sometimes, I never would have been frisky.'

'Men are stupid, Tama,' I gathered up my annoyance at Zabogi and swept it out in a generality.

'Yeah, Ma,' she said, lacing her slim little fingers through mine, 'but we got to make the damn fools feel CHIEF-STUFF, don't we?'

She was laughing now. I felt so relieved to have something to think about other than the agonies of Comma's past and future that I laughed too, almost hysterically.

'What gave you two the crazies?' Zabogi, excluded from our mirth, was galled by it.

'Womens are all crazies, Zabogi,' Tama told him sweetly. 'The only sense that sits down on us is what you mens give us.'

His glare smothered our giggles. 'Make go!' he ordered us. 'I have in my head the village where we will set down our loads for sleep. It is a far walk in front.'

We did not stop at noon. I had learned long ago on other trips that the men were right when they said, 'No one ever travels far on a full belly. The uses of hunger are whips to drive men ahead.'

Tama and I did stop to rest briefly, huddling in the shelter of an uprooted tree.

'Ma,' she asked me, 'are you and Zabogi in a vex? You have a hard eye for each other today.'

'I don't really know,' I said. 'We talked some tells and some tolds before you caught up with us.'

'Talk with Zabogi means that he does all the tolds and the other person don't get to make no tells,' she said. 'But I think from his looks that you made him swallow some tolds, his own self. Oh well, Ma, so God made mens. I put a big rock in his path this morning when I tailored that lie about my bad dream. I did it so the other men would laugh at him. A man don't like to have other mens laugh at him. I wanted to small him down.'

'Well, he tailored an answer big enough to cover his shame,' I reminded her.

'I wouldn't make other mens laugh at Comma.' She said this as though to herself, wonderingly.

'That's because Comma doesn't swell himself up to be a big man,' I said. 'Comma doesn't need to be smalled down.'

'You're wrong, Ma. Comma swells himself up to be bigger than anyone. When he says to himself, he is all wrapped up like a bed blanket in big thinks about the big man he will be when he is a doctor. He sees in his inside eye that when the witch doctor, and even Doctor Harley, cannot make someone well, he will do it with one try. It is the eyes of other people that have made Zabogi big and Comma small. A person soaks up what others put on his skin when they set eye on him. Everyone who ever looked at Comma looked orphan-ness into him. It grew into him like the chop he ate. All of Comma's big thinks cannot rid the orphan out of him.'

'What help is there, then, for Comma?' I asked her. 'I see no good ahead for him anywhere unless he can make his big thinks come true.'

She laughed, a secretive delicate little laugh like the tinkle of an ankle bracelet beneath a *lappa*. 'Oh, Ma,' she said. 'You don't know one thing about mens, not one thing. All Comma needs is a *woman to make himself her care.*'

I took hold of both her shoulders and made her look straight at me. 'Tama, no woman must stand between Comma and the only thing he has got left to live for, which is learning.'

She looked straight back at me. 'Ma, you got the good heart, but sometimes your head is empty of sense.'

I tried to make common cause with her. 'We both want what is best for Comma,' I said. 'We just have different ideas about what is best, isn't that it, Tama?'

'You just got the wrong idea, that's the way of it. If Comma would go to the big school and get to be a white kind of doctor, not one village in all of Lomaland would let him sit down there or touch one of the people. He could not even keep himself alive.' (Community menaces are poisoned.) 'He could work at the hospital on the plantation, but only as a dresser [attendant]. He could do that now. Or he could work at the Mission the same way. Both ways, he would be working for white people. A white man will sack a black one for no better reason than he gets the wrong shoe on first, soon morning. The black people would already have sacked Comma for good, and long-since. What then would be left for Comma but to die? Even then, our old ones who are the Deads would not allow him to be with them. There is no place, alive or dead, for Comma, but to become one with his own people. He has not got sense to know this. A woman will have to know it for him.'

When Tama spoke, her close-knit little body gathered itself behind her words and tensed with purpose. It was unfortunate, I thought, studying her really lovely profile, that so many yearning eyes had looked such excessive beauty into her.

After a while she said, 'What's the matter, Mommio? You look sick.'

'I am sick with fear,' I said. 'I fear Comma will get so burned that his hand will be of no further use. He might even die.'

'Why, Ma,' she said. 'Comma won't even feel heat. Comma never stole.'

VII

BAD-KPUESI

When the Devil walks,
the night belongs to men.

ZABOGI gave me solemn, pop-eyed assurance that the Kpuesi village where he wanted us to sleep was a bad place, very bad. There was no other we could reach by nightfall, so we would just have to make the poor-best we could of it, he said.

Bad-Kpuesi was so common an expression among my houseboys that I had thought, in the beginning, that it was all one word. Without this deep-rooted hostility between groups which was intensified during the days of slave raids, the many distinct tribes with separate languages could not have persisted in a country as small as Liberia. If you ask any one of them about it, he will tell you that the first man of your informant's tribe came straight from God. This first man, their Adam, had many children, all but one of whom was stupid or evil. The good one became the ancestor of the tribe of which the teller of the moment is a member. The unworthy brothers were dispersed throughout the land with a deplorable set of first women to found the 'bad', or other tribes. You may also learn that the first white man was a regrettable after-thought on the part of the Creator.

'What makes this town where we are to sleep a bad place, besides that it is Kpuesi?' I asked Zabogi.

'Oh, the chief's clerk can read.' I waited for Zabogi to continue, but he did not expand his explanation.

'That makes a town bad? If one man in it can read?'

'Sure, Ma.'

'But why?'

'Ma, did you ever study on a gourd full of palm wine? What is on top, and what is under?'

'Why yes,' I said. Sammi used palm wine instead of prepared yeast to raise our bread. 'On top is suds, all froth and fizz. We skim that off. Underneath is the strong stuff that raises dough.'

'Right,' Zabogi approved. 'Now reading is froth and fizz. It is all air and no stuff. It never grew a big belly on anything. When you stand before this clerk that can read, you will hear him make froth and fizz, all trouble and waste.'

'How shall I speak to him, Zabogi?'

'Talk strong and hard, Ma. Talk lawyer-English. Outlawyer him. He acts like a government man.'

Law is one of the highly esteemed professions in Monrovia. The formal speech of the governing class is therefore called lawyer-English. I had, in order to be understood by my houseboys, learned to speak their pidgin and had delighted in it. A long time had passed since I had found it necessary to speak lawyer-English to anyone. I felt ill prepared to indulge in rhetoricals with a surly clerk.

We found him sitting on the piazza of the chief's house with a big old battered dictionary open across his knees. He wore a threadbare black serge suit, greenish under the arms. He sat with his knees spread, his bare feet pointed inward, the great toes nervously overlapped. He had a wrinkled monkey-face, small for the rest of his body, balanced on a deeply furrowed neck which rose out of an oversize white celluloid collar. Between his small eyes was a flat spread of nose on which he had attempted to clinch a pair of old-time steel-rimmed pince-nez.

'How do you do?' My most formal tone.

He had his finger under the word he was studying. Squinting sideways, I saw it was *Polyxena*. He moved his finger and muttered as he read. A curve of dirty broken fingernail scratched the mildewed paper as he progressed, 'a daughter of Priam and Hecuba, betrothed to Achilles. At their wedding. . . .'

'How do you do?' I said it much louder this time.

He sighed with an elaborate show of weary patience.

'Madam! You are interrupting the nuptials of the gods!'

Muttering again in monotone: 'Paris treacherously slew Achilles. Polyxena was sacrificed to appease his shade. See Hecuba.'

'I want to see the chief!' I believe I was shouting by this time.

'The chief, madam, is not in residence today.' He flipped some pages backwards. 'Let's see, now. Hemp . . . helicon . . . heel . . . heddle, here we are, Hecuba.'

Zabogi was tapping his wooden sandal against the plank floor. He looked ready to burst all his seams.

'Helicon, heel, heddle, HELL!' Zabogi roared. 'Get your feet under you, man, and show some respect for our Ma.'

The pince-nez snapped off the clerk's nose and clattered to the floor. When he bent over to retrieve them, the dictionary slipped off his lap. Nothing dignified for him to do now but to stand up. Zabogi was not one to let go of a temporary advantage.

'We want two houses for the night,' Zabogi demanded. 'Two clean houses, side by each.'

'Under the circumstances, that is not feasible.' I thought the clerk's voice had a slight tremor in it. '*The sacred Poro bush school for this village is about to go into session!* The Big Devil will come to town tonight to catch the initiates. No stranger may stay in the town. Any woman' (looking at me hatefully with an expression just like Town Chief's) 'caught contemplating or spying on the Devil will be put to death. You must know of this custom. It is common in the land.'

Johnny, standing back of me, was tugging at one of my braids – a let's-get-out-of-here signal. Zabogi was peeling out of his country-cloth shirt. I thought he was stripping for action. Instead, he turned around so his bare back was in full view of the clerk.

Zabogi had five rows of neat raised scars running parallel from the nape of his neck to the waistline. He then loosened his trousers and slid them down. A multiple and intricate lacing of scarification spread out below the small of his back across the buttocks.

'Hmmmm!' the clerk said between parted lips and clenched teeth. His teeth were jaundice-yellow like the underlying tone of his skin.

As a man is initiated into successive higher degrees of the Poro, additional rows of scars indicate his rank. Zabogi was a big man in the Poro, and he wore the evidence of his importance on his behind. The Poro cuts across tribal boundaries; a high-ranking Poro official is accorded respect in any tribe.

Zabogi hitched up his pants and faced our reluctant host. 'Well?' Zabogi had 'set his eye hard'.

'Well, certainly,' said the clerk, a whining sycophant now. 'You can all sleep in the rest-house just outside the town. I regret that it is somewhat in disrepair.'

Disrepair? It was filthy. Village goats and fowls had stabled in it and cockroaches had devoured most of the thatch of the roof. Zabogi cursed Kpuesi people and their lack of all good works the entire time the boys were sweeping out. They sprinkled down the clouds of dust that billowed up behind their twig brooms. Then they built a fire on the earth floor of the largest room and found pungent twigs to burn to spice away the barn smell. The smoke left easily through holes in the roof. The place seemed scarcely more spirit-proof or sheltering than the branches of forest trees, but everyone seemed happy to be there except Johnny.

'Do you know what the Devil would do to a Bassau boy?' Johnny asked me in a hoarse whisper.

'Well, I have read,' I said, 'that in the old days, if they caught someone like you, they would feed that person as a sacrifice to the sacred fire in the Poro. But the secret societies are not so strong in Africa as they used to be. Anyway, no mind. Even the Devil's catcher would respect my gun.'

'It is still the old days in Africa, Ma,' he said. 'The secret societies are not less strong; they are only more secret. The white man will find that out some day. If the Devil's catcher found me, he would carry me to the sacred bush and they would cut out my liver while I still breathed. Then all the bad-Kpuesi boys would eat it. This would make them strong so they would not cry when the *Zo* cuts their sticks [ritual circumcision]. Then the *Zo* would cut off my *siree* [genitals] to use for a pointer to point the way to other boys who hide from him.' (This would be in the manner of a divining or dowsing rod. Since the victim's penis 'did not agree' to be cut, it would be thought to possess an affinity toward this member of boys of similar persuasion, and pull the Devil's catcher toward them). 'Don't you look out of the window tonight, Ma, or they will catch even you.'

'I won't look out of the window,' I promised him. 'Just to make sure that my curiosity is not stronger than my manners, I will ask Zabogi to close them tight.'

When I went to talk this over with Zabogi, he had already mended the sagging shutters and secured them with raffia ropes from the outside.

'If anyone has got latrine business to do, let him go to the bush before sundown,' Zabogi warned. 'If anyone thinks he has got to go in the night, he will just have to think himself out of it.'

'If the Devil comes around here,' Johnny said, 'I won't have any thinks strong enough to tie my water. We will just get a wet-down house, that's all.'

Johnny was in such a shiver of fear that he spilled the food he tried to cook. Comma, surprisingly calm, took over the job.

'Tell us again what the clerk said, Ma.' Dika was trying to distract Johnny.

I tried to remember. 'Hemp . . . helicon . . . heel . . . heddle, here we are, Hecuba.'

They practised it until everyone could say it and did, over and over, making monkey faces and mincing the words.

'When the Devil walks, the night belongs to men,' Tama said. 'Women should shiver together. I want to spread my sleeping-mat under your hammock, Ma.'

'That is my rightful place,' Johnny told her. 'You are all the time taking my place beside the Ma. The Devil isn't loose to catch women. He wants uncut boys.'

'I like to be in a room alone,' I said. 'The reason is that I like to read, and also I write down every night what we have done in the day.'

'You would not like to write down that the Poro Devil carried away your Johnny, would you, Ma? And that no one ever put eye on him again?' Johnny looked ready to weep.

'If you have to sleep across the door, then what about Comma?' I argued. 'The Devil has never eaten Comma either. Soon-time, everyone here will have to sleep in my room.'

They looked at each other meaningfully but no one spoke. I realized that everyone there except myself had some know-ledge about this which they were not about to tell me. The silence lengthened awkwardly.

'Give us a story, Ma.' Zabogi had thought of a way out. The men chorused his demand.

'I'm tired,' I begged off. 'I'm going to bed. Tama may sleep in my room. When you all decide to go to sleep, any who fear too much may come inside also.'

Johnny's aplomb was almost restored now that he knew he could sleep in my room. 'Comma – Zabogi – everybody, come on. We got to let the Mommio get dressed for night.'

While I cold-creamed my face, Tama sat on her sleeping-mat, rubbing her throat and arms with a piece of cinnamon-scented bark. Then she took some sort of unguent out of her belongings and began to massage her breasts with brutal vigour.

'Why do you do that, Tama?'

'To break them down,' she said. 'Five children have taken suck from me and still my breasts look like they had never seen the use God made them for. They are as saucy as when I first went into the Sande bush school. It is a shame-palaver.'

After we were settled, the men crept into the darkened room one by one and lay down on the floor.

We heard the Devil late in the night. It was not a terrifying sound – more like someone in the distance blowing across the top of a bottle. I do not believe the dreaded personage entered the village that night at all, but that he was alerted to wait until the following night when we would be gone.

After the first *whoooo*, I felt a tug on the ropes of my hammock.

'Mommio?' It was Johnny's whisper.

'Yes, Johnny?'

'You never put your short gun in bed with you, Mommio.'

'We don't need a gun; we need sleep,' I said, crossly. 'But OK, I'll get it, if you will be more easy.'

'Thank you, Mommio,' he said. 'All right, now. I will let sleep sit on me.'

I crawled out of my hammock and fumbled among my things until I found the .45. Once I was armed we all felt somewhat easier, and finally managed to get to sleep.

VIII

WHO FELLED THE ONE-EYE?

An Ignorant is someone who don't know the same Trues you know.

JOHNNY had us up and coffee-waked well before daylight the next morning. We couldn't show our backs to that Devil-ridden town fast enough to please him.

Termites were flying in spectral clouds as we set out. Had the men been in country they liked, Johnny could not have hindered them from delaying to scoop up a great catch to be fried later in palm oil. Deep-fried termites with salt are crisp crunchy morsels, which in the cooking seem to lose all identity with the insect world. I had never been able to bring myself to look at the carriers when they popped the soft white bodies of grubs into their mouths, but I think almost anyone would relish termites, properly prepared, provided he did not know what he was eating.

'A white person's tongue has its roots in his thinks,' they said, laughing about all the delicacies we miss because of this.

We had seen no game since we started except monkeys. The colony we passed 'belonged' to the nearby village, so I did not dare to shoot. The impy creatures seemed to know this. They pelted us with seed-pods, dangling by one hand to get a better look at us, and chattered a gibberish which seemed to mingle curses with derisive laughter.

Although we had ample rice, the men were meat-hungry.

'If we meet a deer on the path and you are not beside the Ma to set the gun in her hand,' Zabogi threatened the gun bearer, 'we will just eat you instead.'

It was only a grim joke; eating human flesh, except perhaps ritually in the Poro, is probably history along with the inter-tribal wars on which cannibalism thrived, and to which the Liberian Government has put a stop. However, the little gun-toter was sufficiently impressed to dog my heels all day.

We saw no game. The jungle was as quiet as though we were the only life that dared move boldly through it. We could hear faint rustlings near the path – slithery reptilian hints of movement. Constrictor snakes, turtles, lemurs, these and many other inhabitants of an earlier steamier age of the world inhabit these forests, unseen though they were at the moment. What impudence in us, the talking mammals of a later era, to have invaded their forest domain!

The carriers seemed to share something of my feelings of intrusion. They saved their laughter and shouts and songs for the clearings and the areas of low bush, second growth, where the forest was only beginning to recover from human dom-inance. A felting of moss carpeted our footfalls; our own breathing as we hurried forward was irreverently loud in a land that seemed to be holding its breath.

The awesome hush was broken by approaching storm. We heard the roar of rain over the tree-tops before it reached us. The sound had the loneliness and power of a distant freight. One sometimes thinks in the deep jungle of things like trains, doorbells, fire sirens, because wind or the birds or the animals make similar sounds. These machines seem like something out of an unreal and chaotic past. Even when one is miserably cold and wet, the machined world seems in retrospect a super-fluous clutter, which happily one has escaped. The present discomfort is something that has been chosen, and it does not victimize its participants. The wildness and the loneliness become part of you and you feel enlarged by it in a way that would not be possible if the force of the elements were merely observed from a dry comfortable shelter.

The men turned their heads to look at me and laugh the

moment the clouds spilt over us. The deluge released them from the constraining silence; they went forward invigorated. They wanted me to tilt up my chin and laugh with them in the face of the storm. In a moment only Johnny and Dika, the two nearest to me in front, were visible. The others were cloaked by the downpour.

After the sky had lost its burden of water and the sun steamed out, the cavern gloom of the forest floor brightened to bottle-green with shimmerings of filtered chartreuse. Peacock-blue plantain-eaters flashed their dazzling plumage under the lower limbs of trees. Above our heads we heard throaty burbles of pleasure and screams of joy from the feathered world of the tree-tops, partitioned from us by a matting of leaves.

The farmer came out in the Loma men when we skirted clearings where the trees had been felled and the brush burned for rice farms. Ashes from the burning are the 'small bed blankets for the seeds', seeds which should be 'put to bed' before the first rains. In most cases, the rains had come a little too soon.

'Just like those lazy old Kpuesi people,' Zabogi sniffed. 'Just wait until you get to Loma country, Ma. The seed will be all bust, new-green, growing.'

Near almost every village we passed we would see a side path blocked off with a fringe of raffia curtain. This is the indisputable KEEP OUT of the Poro. All through the Kpuesi country, it was the time of cult sessions. Cutting farm is man's work, and that had been done. Brush-cutting contests had been held with carnival zest, winners had been crowned and fêted, but not in time for an early planting.

Planting is done by women. 'Can a man born a *pickin*? No more can he grow rice. Woman is the life-keeper. Seed dropped from a man's hand would only rot and be waste.' No one ever explained to me why a man could not pull weeds. When I asked what disaster that would effect, the women would laugh and the men would change the subject. One chief did tell me with a lecherous grin that 'men's backs need to be kept untired for more important matters'.

Soon now, the women would bend double above the sprouting earth, narrow short-handled hoes in their hands, trying to hold back the jungle until the crop was harvested. Men were free to retire behind the raffia curtains to indulge in religious rites and terrors, terrors so sacred that a woman may not even utter the name of the Big Devil without being punished.

The core of the Poro, a man will tell you if you can get him to speak about it while quite alone with you, is veneration of Earth Mother and 'earth-things'. But men have arranged that while they are worshipping the Great Mother, their women are bending to tillage!

Anywhere one goes in north-western Liberia, one can never be completely unmindful of the Poro cult. Whether passing the raffia screens across paths, or crossing streams on the fantastic suspension bridges of vine which the Devil is supposed to spin out of his body like a spider, or admiring the pattern of scars on a man's back, or hearing the music of pitched whistles coming off a hill at night, the Devil seems omnipresent. I found myself while standing in a clearing enjoying a brief unimpeded glimpse of a patch of sky, fancying the features of the Big Devil's mask of terror (which I had seen at Ganta in Dr. Harley's rare collection) outlined in formations of cloud!

Zabogi pushed us without mercy throughout the day. No matter who complained about what discomfort, his prescription was always rooted in implicit faith in the terrain cure.

'The path that hurts you heals you,' he would say. 'Make go.'

My 'go' was all gone long before we reached the town where he wanted us to sleep. I tried to divert my senses from the drag of fatigue by recalling some scrap of memorable prose to repeat and ponder. But Mind is so easily overwhelmed and dwarfed by the frightening vitality of vegetative abundance in the tropics, it is difficult to prod it into action. The forest was so endlessly green, so choked and matted with tangled growth, that I could not fling my thoughts over and beyond it. Except for my little band of carriers, I seemed to have lost all human company elsewhere in the world and everywhere out of the past. I was depleted. All I could think about was the physical necessity of making one foot and then the other get itself forward. I could strive for nothing except that anonymous mud hut somewhere ahead where I could soak the soreness out of my aching muscles and stretch out, dry and warm, in my hammock with the friendly orange light of a lantern casting its glow on the pages of a meaningful book. Although Matter might triumph by day, Mind would get its innings at evening!

Reading the Old Testament with footnotes supplied by the experiences I had enjoyed among tribes-people was like reading it for the first time. The story of Moses' rod, for instance, could have been lifted right out of hinterland Liberia with only minor variations. The rod would have been a chief's swagger stick covered with leather, ringed with ivory and studded with silver. Cast on the earth, it would have begun with the same facility to twitch and then to wriggle itself into an active awesome serpent which must be quickly caught again by the tail lest a powerful swagger stick be lost to the bush.

Walt Whitman's verse was, I thought, better in a mud hut than it could be any other place in the world. I made that unqualified remark once to Captain H. C. Broti of the S.S. *Delairs*. He smiled tolerantly and said, 'Unless it is on a ship at sea.'

I could imagine Whitman striding these forest trails with a vitality to match the verdure, noting the odour of that thickly composted ancient earth blet with decay, pondering how nature 'distils such exquisite winds out of such infused fetor'.

It seemed a sort of miracle that he could have written, without having trekked to Lomaland on such a day as this one, those lines which were my hope:

> *. . . you smothered ennuis!*
> *Ah think not you finally triumph,*
> *My real self has yet to come forth.*

Emerson seemed to me to be the necessary companion to Whitman. He put into cool perspective the vague sensations and longings which Whitman put into words.

And then there was the *Odyssey!* Had there been a necessity to choose between my guns and ammunition and these four books – The *Bible, Leaves of Grass,* Emerson's *Essays* and Homer's *Odyssey* – I would have unhesitatingly left the weapons behind. Game can be trapped or snared; sustaining thoughts are more elusive. Had I owned the writings of Dr. Albert Schweitzer at that time, I should certainly have considered them indispensable.

Native people as well as ourselves are oppressed by the magnitude of the forests. They have peopled the bush with little gnomes who scrape branches to waken travellers out of this gloomy mood. A stab of fear, they say, will startle your gloom-trussed mind and it will kick itself free of what ties it. One must stay alert, too, to avoid swallowing these little gnomes. They are so small they can be inhaled with a breath of air, but once inside they grow and grow until they entirely possess the mind; their victim has bush-madness. The *ju-ju* against this form of insanity is bound in little packets of leather. My magic was bound between the covers of books. *Ju-ju* can go dead in a crucial moment, leaving one destitute. I found that this was also true of a book. Those that failed me on other trips were so sharply disappointing that I was never able to re-sample them under more favourable conditions. Usually, it was some intimation of insincerity that repelled me. In a mud hut with only the lantern and the mosquito netting and woollen blankets for luxuries, one is living so close to the margin of necessities that this one flaw is immediately conspicuous and ruins the whole.

At last, we reached that village toward which Zabogi had been herding us. We stood dripping and shivering before the ceremonious chief, exchanging compliments and *dashes*. When that was over, the village women had our bath-water hot and fires burning briskly on the floors of two adjacent huts.

These villagers were intensely curious. The women crowded into my hut and would not budge while I had my bath. They amused themselves by making derogatory remarks about my figure. Their gestures indicated my deficiencies, fore and aft, while from among their own groups they pointed out specimens of pulchritude who were obviously more lavishly endowed.

A mole-like birthmark, to which I have never paid much attention, was the object of their concerted dismay. They felt it, exclaimed, and showed me by slowly inching their fingertips away from it how it would spread in all directions, growing until it covered me like a pelt of brown moss. I took a careful look at the thing myself. Slightly larger than I remembered? Might not be a bad idea to have it checked? Oh, nonsense! Old wives' tales! Later, at the plantation hospital the doctor explained that he would have to go rather deep – those things sometimes spread.

The women were still jabbering at me when Johnny brought my dinner. Knife-and-fork eating amazed them. Again by gestures, they showed me how much more efficient it is to convey rice to the mouth in compact little balls rolled in the fingers. It was all good fun and I would have enjoyed them had I not been so bone-tired. All I wanted was to be alone with the reading I craved. Here was the shelter, but where was the solitude? When?

Privacy is something for which a tribesman never seems to feel a need. Special people do go off by themselves in the forest for special purposes – the tribal carver to make sacred ritual masks, the medicine man to gather herbs, the bewitched to produce magical wrack of village good, 'spoiling God's plan'. But in ordinary affairs, they cannot conceive of anyone wanting to be alone. As usual, that night I was outmanoeuvred.

'You ready to catch us in ink?' Johnny asked. 'All right! I ready to give you back our day.'

Tama had already settled her belongings with mine.

Johnny had talent for mimicry and pantomime. The day he started to 'give me back' promised to be so hilarious that Tama slipped over to the carriers' hut to beckon them in to listen.

The incident he pounced on to make the most of concerned Dika, our redhead, who had felt an overpowering need to step off the path to urinate. Zabogi had refused him this privilege, thinking that Dika was only making excuse to set down his load and rest a bit. Zabogi had booted Dika from behind, both with caustic remarks and a hastening nudge in the seat with the toe of his wooden sandal. Then, deciding to add example to precept, Zabogi had edged ahead of Dika to demonstrate a proper stride. What happened to Zabogi as he passed Dika was exactly what might have been expected under the circumstances. The proverb which Johnny built out of it was that 'some things are wetter than rain'.

After Johnny's recital I thought they would surely be ready to rest. But no! They must have something from me to cap their day. I decided to give them a short, very short summary of the *Odyssey*.

Poor Ulysses! Twenty years away from his people! None of them had ever stayed at the plantation through more than one rice-planting.

Ah, Calypso, eh? So! Ulysses had been dallying in a cave with Calypso! For seven years? Latoka admitted that he might,

nder irresistible inducements, dally with a woman not of his
ibe for one night, but not for long, not after his sense caught
p with him. (The foreignness of the woman, not the dalliance,
as the shocking part of this confession.) That Calypso must
ave bought her love-medicine from a powerful *Zo*. How
d Ulysses escape from her at all? Did her love-medicine go
:ad? Was Calypso a free mamma? (Free in the sense that she
elonged to no man.)

Zabogi put forth that what Ulysses felt for the wench was
ily body-hunger. He expounded the same theory he had
:esented to me earlier, commenting on Tama. Heart-hunger,
ie true love that is strongest when a person gets some sense
id some years on him, had grown strong in Ulysses. Heart-
inger for Penelope, Ulysses' true woman, was finally
:onger than the *gris-gris* of Calypso.

Penelope's character was thoroughly analysed. Was Pene-
·pe frisky? If not, why didn't she get rid of those suitors her
·vn self? Friskiness seemed a delicate subject to discuss in
ama's presence but she jumped right into the argument,
:fending Penelope. If Penelope were frisky, why would she
ouble herself to weave a gravecloth for a husband who might
ill be alive? *Aye, yah!* What with all the work a woman has
do, only the Goods in her could get her to ravel out by night
hat she had accomplished by day.

Dika announced that he was going to change the name of
s dog to Argus because it had more sense than most people.
st think Argus knew Ulysses after twenty years. That scar
ι Ulysses' leg that he got hunting a wild boar, was that his
ιly distinguishing mark? Had a brave man like that gone
ιmarked by the Poro?

Refunding the dower was a problem with which several
' them had had personal and bitter experience. Sacrificing a
ιllock was, of course, the proper way to make medicine for
long and important journey. The augur who prophesied
ɔm the flight of birds came in for severe criticism. Their own

Zos could have apprenticed that augur to his benefit. Th
proper way to divine was by sheep's entrails or a dowsing-ro
('smelling-stick') or a pot of sand. Those bad winds presse
into leather bags! Some fool Kpuesi must have been in th
crew to undo the ties!

Thus for four nights we held session with one of the 'grea
books' in what must have been one of the few times a class
has been given such a thorough and enthusiastic going ove
in pidgin.

That first night when I 'gave them Ulysses' we got onl
as far as the adventure with the Cyclops. We lived ourselv
into the story a bit too vividly.

I sat in my hammock; the men sat on the floor groupe
around my feet. Our lantern hung from a thong tied to on
of the sapling roof-poles to which the hammock was als
secured. Every time I shifted my weight, the lantern bobbe
wildly and the shadows of the men shifted drunkenly. Behin
me, the fire crackled on the earth floor. Johnny had kept th
bath-warming fire going, insisting that the smoke going u
into the roof-peak would smoke out any rats who lived the
and also any snakes who might come in to catch the rats.

The fire flickering and flaring on the cylindrical mud wal
gave the room an eerie cave quality. My own shadow on th
curved surface was a hunched giant whose head was lost
the conical darkness of the roof-peak. It was too warm in th
hut after the men trooped in, closing the only door behin
them. The dank closeness of the air was grotto-like, too.
was a perfect setting for the story and I had a good tale to te
I gave it my all, which turned out to be a little too much. A
I talked their mouths dropped flatteringly agape, as thoug
the essence of the tale were something exotic to be tasted o
the tongue.

As Ulysses left his ship and approached the cave throug
the horrid shade (was it saw-grass?), I saw my audience tighte
their arms around their raised knees. Suspense about wh

Ulysses would find in the land of a strange tribe seemed to pull their buttocks off the floor. Their eyes were big and animal-bright in the orange lantern glow, the whites showing, as they went along with Ulysses and his twelve bravest men, exploring the Cyclops' cave, waiting, bold but frightened, holding themselves tight against the giant's return.

Even to me, the wooden trail-cases stacked against the wall became the bending shelves of the Cyclops' well-stocked larder, the carrying *kinjas*, the 'wicker baskets heap'd'. A goat bleated outside our cave-hut like a kid strayed from the one-eyed savage's flock. An old lumpy rice-bag was projected in shadow into the enormous boulder sealing us into the cave with the raving blinded monster.

There was no escape. Which two of them would be the next to be devoured? They looked at each other, their eyes rolling with terror, each hoping it would be the man next, or next, but not oneself. There was no hope anywhere, except as it came from the story. No matter how they 'sharpened all their thought' like the mortals in the story, they couldn't get out of that stone-sealed cavern. Only the story knew; only by hearing it out, by reaching the end, could they buy release from the clutching hairy hands now exploring every cranny, reaching, flailing, searching. . . .

At that high moment, a rat who must not have minded smoke came bounding down out of the thatch. None of us saw it or thought about it being a rat. What we heard was a rustling, a bump, a fearful clatter. My cosmetic case, sitting atop some stacked cases, was knocked to the floor with an awesome crash of jars and breaking bottles. But we didn't know that either. It was the Cyclops, uprooting furniture in impotent rage and pain.

Latoka, the wizened little fellow who had ripped the insides out of live elephants, dreamed about it almost every night, sprang to do battle with a new and larger foe. He grabbed a burning log and started to flail as blindly as though he too

had lost his sight. Sparks and screams flew through the hut.
The lantern chimney was smashed on the first wild swing,
the glass chiming to the floor in the darkened room.

My hammock turned over during the pandemonic uproar,
and I was dumped on the floor. Someone stepped heavily on
my back and then, being caught in his lunge by the barrier
of hammock, toppled over me. From the depth of the groan
and the weight, I judged it to be Zabogi.

The only voice I could distinguish clearly in the uproar
was Comma's. 'No fear! No fear! Give pause, now.' His voice
was necessarily loud, but it sounded as calm as the day he
had first caged old Town Chief. 'No fear. Everyone lie down
on the floor! Give me that fire-club, Latoka.'

Somehow, his quietness quieted them. Latoka relinquished
the burning club to Comma over several prostrate, panting
forms. Comma quietly laid it back in the fire and stirred up
a little more light. 'Bring the other lantern from the carrier
hut, Johnny,' he said.

'I can't.' The muffled voice was only vaguely Johnny's.
'Somebody's behind thinks my head is a chair.'

'I'll get it,' Comma said. 'Everyone stay where he is until
I get back. Don't move.'

'Everyone but the man with his behind on my bent-over
ear,' Johnny amended the order.

That broke the spell. They laughed. Laughter rolled the
stone from the cave. They were all whole, none badly hurt,
miraculous as it seemed, none burned.

'It was only a story,' Comma said. 'A never-never-story.
You ought to know that, Latoka. It is not true.'

'Oh, shut up, Comma.' Latoka was a little ashamed of his
frenzy, I think. 'It was so, a *true*. It takes true-thing to make
my heart believe that my ears are a drum! People who go
around knocking down the Trues ought to get knocked down
their own selves so they would know the feel of it.'

'Everyone here, save only one old rat, knows the feel

getting knocked down,' Johnny said, vigorously rubbing his ear. 'Shut up, your own self, Latoka.'

'Give us the rest of the story, Ma,' Dika demanded. 'I can't sleep if I don't know the way out of that cave.' In his excitement, he had run his hands through that amazing mop of red hair until it seemed ready to crackle with the sparks for which he was named.

'Not tonight,' I said firmly. 'Next sundown.'

'I'm going to sleep in here with you, Ma,' Johnny announced. 'Before sun comes, I will get that old rat.'

Zabogi eyed him sarcastically. 'And the One-Eye, too, uh? The Ma has got to watch with both eyes to keep the One-Eye off you?'

Johnny got the rat. Not just one, but three enormous creatures. He baited them with a crust of scorched rice from our cooking-pot. The terrifying thing about them, to me, was that they approached like big tame cats without showing any fear or timidity whatever. I remembered hearing that at the well-run Episcopal Mission nothing they had been able to do prevented rats from invading the dormitory and chewing the soles of the sleeping children's feet. After Johnny had clouted the rats with a fire-club, we watched hordes of vermin desert the bodies.

From the wet stains in my cosmetic case, an overwhelming concentration of 'Pink Clover' fumed through the hut. I dreamed that I was back in Iowa where a summer breeze fanned the aroma off a hay-field. I was 'Maud Muller on a summer's day', fetchingly decked out in an airy ballet outfit which certainly would have startled John Greenleaf Whittier! Also my father toward whom I was dancing with his mid-afternoon lunch! The silver-green willows along the creek swayed and dipped accompaniment as I twirled my toes on clover blossoms big as dahlias which supported my weight, unbending. But when we opened the lunch-basket, there was nothing inside but a dead rat. I screamed, waking myself and

Johnny. His hand fumbled under my mosquito netting reaching for my forehead.

'There, there, Mommio,' he consoled me. 'No fear th One-Eye. No old One-Eye sits down here.'

I clutched his sturdy little hand. 'It's not the One-Eye Johnny. It's those awful rats!'

Johnny patted my arm. 'Oh, but Mommio, those rats can' hurt you. They are all dead. It is only the One-Eyes that w got to watch out for.'

'I'm sorry I woke you, Johnny.'

'Oh, that's all right, Mommio. Don't feel shame becaus the Fears got hold of you. Everybody has got the Fears. Som people just got different ones than other people, that's all. just wish Ulysses had killed the old bad One-Eye though.'

It really was not rational to be phobic of rats, especiall dead ones, I told myself. Johnny had the reasonable view; i is the One-Eyes we need to fear. We don't call them Cyclop any more, of course. We have Englished the name of one o those life-diminishers to Colour-prejudice. I think him clan chief of the odious horde.

The *Odyssey* came out the right measure for the journey On the sixth night, we got the big bow into Ulysses' hands watched him inspect it to see whether bug-a-bugs 'had don the weapon wrong', watched the trembling string as the maste drew the mighty bow with ease. Lightning flashed and thunde rolled over our heads just as it did in the tale while we hear the whizzing arrow, and saw it 'threading every ring'.

'If we were not going home to Boitai,' Zabogi said, ' would be sorry that we lack small to reach. That Ulysse must have been part Loma.'

'I think Ulysses was part every-man,' I said 'That's wh we all like him.'

Zabogi was quiet for rather a long interval. 'Yeah, Ma,' h said finally, softly. I would like to believe that Zabogi, wh certainly had never thought of himself as a unit of any grou other than the Loma tribe, may have felt, just fleetingly, some intimations of universality. At least, he had wholeheartedly accepted a hero not born in Lomaland, a concession in itself.

Before we started walking on the final day of the trip, Zabogi asked me to sit down in my hut while he threw some sense to the carriers. The speech was eloquent, authoritative, and in Loma. Since I could hear it all and understood none of it, I should have liked to watch the gestures that must have accompanied such stentorian words.

'Your talk leaves me out,' I heard Johnny grumble when Zabogi had finished the harangue. 'When there is talk, I like to be inside it.'

'You are our stranger,' Zabogi told him kindly. 'If you make some small mistake, we will not hold you hard. But these others will soon be home, home in Boitai. I gave them their manners. Some have been gone too long. They have been white mens and government people and bad-Kpuesis, and all kinds of bad coast ways. I don't want bad ways to be part of the cargo we carry into Boitai.'

'We reach today?' Johnny asked.

'Today!' Zabogi was roaring with happiness. 'Today, the seven-day, we reach.'

'Seven is my luck number.' Johnny was bubbly with anticipation.

'That's just an ignorant native superstition.' Comma's voice was in pedantic cadence. 'There are no luck numbers. There is only a bad-luck number. It is thirteen.'

'Oh, goat innards!' Johnny's voice was deep with contempt now.

'Since you have got to talk English, talk easy-English,' Zabogi commanded. 'I like to be inside talk, my own self. What is a superstition? I don't know that one. I don't know ignorants, either.'

'I'll tell you,' Johnny volunteered. 'I studied on that word "superstition" after I heard white people use it all the time.

A superstition is a true something that a black man knows and a white man won't believe.'

'It is not!' Comma retorted. 'A——'

'I'll tell you about that word ignorant, also,' Johnny interrupted him hotly. 'An "ignorant" is someone who don't know the same Trues you know. All white people are Ignorants.'

'*They are not!*' Comma's voice was crackling with anger.

Johnny backed down, but only a little. 'Well, all white are Ignorants, save only a few, like Dr. Harley up at Ganta. He just threw old Time out in the bush like it was a spoiled butter pear [avocado], and gave his ear to black people, so he is not ignorant any more. He knows plenty of Trues. That is why black people all over Liberia are big in their hearts for him. No one likes Ignorants, no matter what colour skin they got.'

'You are ignorant about white people, Johnny.' Comma's voice was rasping toward restraint.

'Humph!' Johnny snorted. 'I know more about white people than they know about their own selves. They like me, that's what they do. And they wouldn't like me if I were an Ignorant, because nobody likes Ignorants.'

'You *Johnny* everything you say,' Comma complained. 'When you finish, it is all Johnny, and people forget the true that you have covered up.'

'That is the thing that makes me a Character,' Johnny bragged. 'I heard some planter mens tell the Mommio that Johnny was some character. White people like Characters. If you are a Character and know your work, you can go any place you want. When we get back, I am going to work for old Ants.'

'And leave the Mommio?' Comma was incredulous.

'Yep,' Johnny said. 'I am wasted at the house of the Mommio. Everyday, God blesses me with great big fine ideas about how to humbug white people. I love the Mommio, and don't want to humbug her. So, I will have to go where my ideas can be of use.'

'You two can waste all your big ideas about how to humbug each other,' Zabogi told them. 'I tire with all your palaver. Johnny acts more like a Loma than you do, Comma. You can just leave all your "not-so's" out here in the bush. We only got room for the "so's" in Boitai.'

'When I get to be a doctor,' Comma said, 'and you come to me with the side of your face all eaten away with yaws so people can see right into your mouth even when it is shut, and your toes have all dropped off where jiggers have hatched out under the nails, and your fingers are all gone with leprosy, and your private parts are so swollen that you will have to make a sling to keep them off the ground because the elephantiasis is so far gone in you, then you will beg me for medicine. And I will withhold the medicine until I tell you again how you lacked to show me respect now.'

'I know some private parts that show promise to need a sling, and they don't belong to me.' Zabogi was not the least appalled by Comma's dire prophecy, though his description did not exaggerate the plight of some victims of these diseases. 'Tie your mouth and stand under your load. Tonight we take chop with our own people. Aye, man!'

'Oh, Zabogi,' Latoka said, 'when you give the journey to our people, will you tell them how we were trapped in a cave with a big old horrible One-Eye, and how I, the brave Latoka, killer of elephants, felled the One-Eye with a fire-club?'

'You did not so, Latoka!' Johnny was feeling too deedy to let that pass. 'I felled the One-Eye. I, Johnny the Character, felled the One-Eye with a laugh. One-Eyes waste to little old nothings when people laugh at them.'

'Seems to me, and as I remember,' Zabogi was speaking lowly as befits a wise man cutting a palaver: I could imagine him rolling his big eyes and scratching his head as though remembered things make the scalp itch – 'seems to me that *Comma felled the One-Eye with a scrap of sense.*'

IX

ANYWHERE IS SOMEWHERE

*Before a man stretches out in a big reach, he
better have his feet on something solid.*

As soon as we passed from Kpuesi territory into Loma,
everything did look better, just as Zabogi had predicted.
The towns had a spruced, cared-for appearance. More
of the house doors were carved, more walls were decorated
with murals done in coloured clays, more of the cooking-pots
were patterned. Everywhere, drums pounded welcome.

The men were a little ashamed that I did not travel in a
hammock suspended under a frame, each of the four corners
resting on a man's head. A chief travels that way, reclining
majestically under covering of leopard pelts and country
cloths, while he slowly fans himself with an elephant-tail
sceptre, badge of the chief-office. Bell-ringers go in front,
praise-singers follow, and the hammock men prance in unison
like trained and spirited horses. The carriers would have liked
for me to have gone accoutred as splendidly as the Queen of
Sheba setting forth to visit Solomon. There was not much
prestige in carrying for a woman who insisted in moving over
the trail on her own mud-spattered feet. Johnny had an idea
for covering the shame of my lack of hammock transportation.

'Tell them hammocks are taboo for her,' he urged Zabogi.
'That will raise your head.'

'How would anyone get that kind of taboo?' Zabogi knew
he would have to back up the statement.

'Oh, tell them that her grandmother was lying asleep in a

hammock on the piazza one day when the town monkeys
came into the village to do all mischief. The monkeys upset
the hammock, and spilled the poor old grandmother on the
floor. This woke her up too soon, and her dream-soul did not
have time to get back in her mouth before she was awake.
Now, all that woman's family have hammock for their
taboo.'

Zabogi was intrigued. 'What happened to the poor old
grandmamma? Was she crazy ever after or did the dream-
soul find its way back?'

'Oh, it was a trouble, I tell you!' Johnny was inspired to
further invention. 'All her children were marked because of
it. They are marked by the Forgets. Our Mommio forgets
where she has put her keys, she forgets which is the market
day in each village and she forgets all the Bassau language I
tell her unless she writes it down. *That is why she has to write
the whole time!* Monkeys caused her all that trouble. Also, that
is why she won't eat monkey meat. Everything about a
monkey tastes bad to the Mommio. But then, there are some
good things about her Forgets.'

'What could be good about the Forgets? I sure don't want
any part of them. I am just stuffed with all that ever reached
me. That is why I grew so big.'

'Well, the good about her Forgets is this,' Johnny explained.
'After I do some small thing that vexes her, I tell her I am
sorry too much. Then she just laughs and says, "No mind,
we'll just forget all about it." Now, I count that a rather large
good.'

Comma, who had also listened in on this exchange, had no
admiration for Johnny's quick imagery.

'Johnny,' he said, 'it is more easy for you to lie than to
breathe.'

'Thank you, Comma. Thank you plenty!' Johnny was
flattered into dipping his buttocks earthward, a small bow of
gratitude.

'It's a sin, that's what it is!' Comma stormed. 'A heavy, terrible-bad sin.'

'Now, Comma,' Johnny said soothingly, 'there are two kinds of lies. The bad kind puts saw-grass and thorns in the path. I don't tell that one. The good kind of a lie just makes people feel good. It makes everything smooth as palm oil. Now what all the people in the whole world need is more good lies. There is more good in one glad lie than in a whole rice bag full of old sour vexed Trues. Good lies hold up a scrap of True and make it shine!'

Johnny walked beside Zabogi whenever the path was wide enough for two to go abreast. Their discussion of Liberian geography yielded the impression that Bassau and Loma territories are the only areas of opulence, lands where large fields of rice crackle and burst with supercharges of nourishment, where the people all go decently clad in brilliant new country cloth, no tattered garments ever being seen, where the cooking-pots are always full, the villages populous and immaculate. Kpuesi country was delineated as a vast poverty-pinched desolation separating the impeccable Bassau and Loma nations. Over to our far right, Gio country was depicted littered knee-deep with bleached human bones, discarded relics of cannibal orgies. They agreed that the only reason the Gios are taller and stronger than other tribesmen is that their ancestors for generations have battened on the 'sweet meat of man'.

Mano country was better than Gio, Johnny asserted with the authority of a much-travelled man (he had been there with me when I walked to Ganta). Still, Zabogi reminded him, the Manos have that cult of leopard men! They stalk their human prey on stilts which leave leopard-like tracks, and they wear on their hands clever gadgets of hinged iron so that the clawed victims will seem to have been pawed by a leopard. (Only the heart is taken from the body; it is the 'big medicine' to be bound in leather and worn by the new owner, adding the strength of the former possessor to his.) That is rather a bad custom, Johnny conceded, but all in all, Manos are all right and only a few of them are leopard men.

Zabogi aided Johnny in searching out similarities between their respective tribes and both of them carefully skirted their differences. What they did not mention is that the Bassaus have only attenuated cult societies while the Loma have the most vigorous of Poro cults and are credited with having introduced the Poro into Liberia. Johnny was blessed with some handsome 'Forgets' himself. Among them was the memory of how violently he had opposed a Loma coming under our roof at the time I hired Comma. To see Johnny now, radiant with pride over his firm friendship with an important Loma, a Poro-marked man in line for a chiefship, was an almost unbelievable sight. Each of them had expanded his isolationism to include one tribe not his own.

There is a stream about thirty minutes' walk from Boitai where Zabogi called a halt so the men could bathe and spruce themselves up for a triumphant entry. Johnny had been saving his canary-gold steward's uniform against this moment, and a gold cap which fitted over one of his perfect front teeth. The men plunged into the stream, boisterously celebrant, spouting jets of water out of their mouths, shouting and shaking themselves and splashing. Only Comma avoided the water. He sat on the bank with his back against the money-crate, his chin sunk to his chest. Comma's gloom was one of the things that bound me to him; it was a white gloom. I eased down beside him, saw that he had been noiselessly weeping.

'Comma, do you fear to bathe now because you almost drowned the first night of our trip?'

'Oh, no, Mommio, it was not the river that caught me.'

'What then?' I could not believe that he would think the Deads had tugged at him, as Tama did.

'It was myself that sunk me! I thought of the long road

ahead, the hard times, if I am to become a white kind of doctor. I couldn't feel the bottom of the river with my feet. I thought of how it is the same way with myself. Everything I try to stand on just moves out from under me. I thought if I just let go of everything, maybe I could get hold of peace. Do you think that Deads' Town and heaven are the same place, Mommio?'

He had attempted suicide! I should have guessed this without having to be told. I knew him to be a strong swimmer. I had admired his stroke as often as I had watched him glide through water. We had a favourite swimming spot on the plantation, a pool in the river Du, bowered with pandanus and palms. Johnny always led the clamour of the houseboys to go along on our picnic-swims; he was sure I could not distinguish a sleeping crocodile from an old log. After the boys had put cassava to roast in a fire and made their crocodile-inspection, they would sport in the water like porpoises, rolling and looping with sure skill and grace. I certainly should have realized that only a great weight of despair could have sunk Comma in that nothing of a river. He had now endured the further humiliation of having to tell me what I should have been perceptive enough to have known.

'I was asking you about heaven.' He looked at me trustfully, sure I could give confident answers. 'Is it the same place that black people call Deads' Town? Is it all one?'

'I am sure that it is, Comma. But if you think one needs to die to get hold of peace, you are wrong! I think you have built your dreams too high. If you would small down your ambition, you would be happier.'

This was not what he expected from me. 'You talk like an African,' he said, glumly, accusingly.

This jarred me. I, a blaster of hope? I believe to the core of my being in each individual achieving the highest self-fulfilment of which he is capable. Why then, I asked myself, did I dare to suggest to Comma that he abandon the dreams he lived by? Should I not be rallying his confidence, urging him on, even to the impossible? Instead, I felt like begging his forgiveness because people of my country had started all that ferment in his mind, and leavened it with encouragement.

Comma was speaking again. 'The Lomas have a saying that the tree who thinks about the top of the forest instead of looking to its roots will blow down in a breeze.'

It came to me then that we sometimes forget in the United States, in our emphasis on the importance of the individual, that no one can achieve full selfhood except in a society which has as a basic principle the *right* of the individual to rise, if he can, above the group level, the permission of those on the level for him to climb above them, even their admiration as he does so. In a communal society, the impudent heads which insist on popping up above the ancient retaining levels of accepted form are screeded off. The squeegeeing process, no matter how brutal, is also considered a right! Looking into Comma's troubled eyes, I read the tragedy of a longing for individual freedom which is *not* insured by a community of free men. In the case of tribal Africans, it is not a dictator, not an all-powerful state, which keeps them in servitude, but the authority of the massed dead, as their memories are perpetuated and eternalized in the Poro. I have never realized more poignantly than at that moment what it means to have been born in a democracy, to have the *right* to achieve. I also realized why I had finally dared to speak to Comma, as he bitterly charged, 'like an African'. The conviction had been slowly forming in me on this trip that where these rights do not exist, ambition is a siren lute to destruction. Can man dream to his peril, even if the dreams are splendid, far-flung, and clean? Unless he dreams in a *climate of freedom,* his dreams are only the mirages of a doomed, desert-lost soul. We honour our great men, rightly. But those in whom we should truly and deeply exult are the ordinary fellow beings who gave them a hand up along the way.

Comma was still thinking of the tree that should look to its roots. 'Before a man stretches out in a big reach, he should have his feet on something solid,' he said. 'I guess I started to reach too far, too soon. Maybe all I should wish for is a place to stand among my own people? Is that what you were trying to tell me, Mommio?'

It was, exactly. Some will criticize me for it, sensing as I did that I had it in my power that moment to sway him either way, toward his people, who resist innovation, or away from them toward what we consider enlightenment. We can have no intelligent argument about this if you have never taken yourself to live for a while to a land where individual freedom is not a prized right.

'Comma, under what roof will you sleep in Boitai?' I suspected that part of his dread of entering the village came from not knowing where he would be welcome.

'I don't know,' he confessed miserably. 'For you, a stranger and a white, there will be a house swept and waiting, a fire burning. For me, also somewhat a stranger, white in some of my ways, the doors may all be shut. My mother will welcome me, but her house is subject to the wishes of Falali, the chief. It seems to me lately that I have been trying to stand with one foot on each of two slippery roofs and I have fallen on my face between them.'

He pointed to the carriers cavorting in the stream.

'Do you know why they are so happy, Mommio? Why they shout so glad that we can scarcely hear each other? It is because each one of them *belongs* somewhere. It is of no matter where. Anywhere is somewhere!'

'Comma,' I said, 'Zabogi told me how Falali, the chief, lost Bola to the blacksmith in a play-gamble debt before you were born. Does Bola stay all the time with Falali now? Zabogi told me some of the money was owing.'

'Only a little part remains unpaid.' Pride showed in his tear-rimmed eyes. 'I, myself, redeemed Bola when I was last in Boitai. She stays all the time now with her true husband, Falali the chief. And, oh Mommio! She is ever big with glad! I had to borrow part of the money but I will earn it all, and pay what little remains.'

'How much of that old gambling debt was still owing to your father?'

'In all those years Falali had only paid a small part, however much he wanted Bola back with him. Falali is just not clever with money!'

'But exactly how much was still owing?' I persisted.

'*Fifty dollars*,' He looked at his feet.

It is the African way of speaking to talk in riddles or proverbs or folk-tales, or failing any suitable ones of these, to say an important thing in an oblique way. I thought Comma was telling me what he had done with that lost money, that like a true tribesman he had been willing to do anything he could for his mother, and that he was now steeling himself for the consequences. I wanted to dig a little deeper, to ask him whether he thought that theft would be justified if in some way it benefited the Virgin Mary. That is the kind of round-about, face-saving question that will yield the largest fund of information from a tribesman. But he had clouded over again with his separateness, so I saved the question for a later time when it might reach him.

'Comma, listen to me!' He started as though he had entirely forgotten my presence. 'I am not going to allow that trial! *There is no need for it now*. Let's call the whole thing off.'

To my surprise, his whole body went slack with disappointment. 'Why, Mommio, that's all we came for.'

Zabogi was shouting at the men: 'Come on, get out now! It was on the drums that we will be at the waterside of Boitai when the sun stands over the big bedi tree!'

I don't know how Zabogi knew the position of the sun, Fog sagged over the tree-tops like a drooped sheet of soiled canvas.

Zabogi charged down at us. 'Ma, let us study ourselves in the glass that gives a person back to himself – the one in your black bag that has your medicine-for-face.'

We set my cosmetic case up on a stump and they preened before the mirror in the lid, trying on new black velvet embroidered pillbox hats they had purchased at exorbitant prices from an itinerant Mandingo trader we had met on the trail. They donned many of the gifts they were taking to their families, tying gaudy head-cloths around their necks like scarves or wrapping them around their hips. There was one vial of perfume in my case that had not been broken the night Latoka 'fought' the Cyclops. I opened it and put a drop on on each proffered ear-lobe, after which they sniffed each other delightedly. Assorted as we appeared, we went forward to Boitai reeking of the same fragrance.

Aroused by their interest in appearances to take a look at myself, I was dismayed. The overdoses of atabrin I had been taking to control the malaria had tinted my skin a mustard hue. I was hollow-eyed with fatigue and my clothes looked awful, because my frail garments never entirely dried at night. The men attached them to sticks which they bound to the cases like miniature flag-poles, the garments fluttering out over their heads as they went down the trail. Nothing a white woman owns looks any sillier than a filmy under-something clinched to a rough twig with home-rolled rope, swooping between the narrow confines of the vine-curtained walls of a forest path. Watching my laundry go ahead of me up a rise of ground, it seemed attached to a flying clothes-line which might at any moment break loose like a kite to undulate above the forest until it snagged on the top of the tallest tree. A quick shower; everything wadded up any old way to keep it from getting soaked again! There was no need to ask the mirror on the stump who was the fairest of us all. Any one of them in his near-nakedness seemed more groomed than I. I was the dowd.

'I look terrible,' I told Zabogi. 'Wait until I find a bright scarf or something.'

He regarded me as though in complete agreement with my estimate. Then his rubbery lips responded happily to an idea in his head.

'Comb out your long hair,' he advised. 'That is the thing about you that is not awkward. Undo your braids and let Johnny brush you until the hair stands out all around you.'

My hair is coarse and straight, but they thought it was wonderful. They sat around watching while Johnny curried me, using their time to twirl little toothbrushes of fuzzed-out sticks against their teeth.

'I wish I had my gold *lappa*,' Tama wailed. 'The Ma has got fine hair and everyone else has got fine cloth to cover them, and I have nothing fine at all to wear.'

I had a *lappa*-length of velvet, ripe egg-plant in colour, in my *dash* chest. I intended it for Bola.

'Shall I?' I cupped my hand to Zabogi's big ear and whispered. Since he knew about that treasure, I thought I ought to confer with him before I gave it to his wife instead of his mother.

He nodded and whispered back. 'Give it to Tama if you like. Bola is so bright with mother-shine, she don't need new cloth to look fine!'

The velvet was only a little brighter than Tama's skin. She draped it around her so the bottom edge hiked up just enough to reveal the brass anklet she had been polishing with sand. She had a gold bangle around her neck and large gold ear-rings; she was all resplendent in purple and gold, not the least of which was the plum-purple of her own shining skin. She carefully outlined her lips with a cube of laundry bluing, and it seemed a better choice for her, more in key, than a red lipstick would have been. Tama's lips were scarcely more everted than mine and she habitually held them slightly parted which added to the eager expectancy of her expression. She revolved on her toes like a mannequin for all of us to see the final effect, a sad little pirouette as though there were sadness in beauty, the sadness part of the beauty. The men did not cheer; they just sucked in their breath through their mouths and regarded her with the same melancholy dignity which emanated from her. Comma did not so much as glance toward us.

'You look fine, Tama,' Zabogi admitted grudgingly. 'Fine, too much! Come on now! Make go!' He was jigging with happiness as he helped the men up with their loads for the last time.

'Zabogi,' I suggested, 'why don't you take those filthy, nasty, half-dead chickens off Tama's head and take that heavy *kinja* off her back, so she can walk free into Boitai in her fine clothes?'

'When I get to be a chief, I will have many wives,' he said. 'Then I can afford to have one who carries nothing. Tama will only need to clap her hands and the young wives will come running to do whatever she orders. But for now, Tama must carry loads.'

When I looked again, Comma had somehow boosted the fouled wicker chicken-coop on top of the money-chest and he had her *kinja* strapped on his own back.

'See?' I pointed it out to Zabogi.

'Comma's a fool,' Zabogi said grimly.

'Who's the fool?' I asked him sharply.

Zabogi grinned as cheerfully as though he had just scored a point in a jolly game of riddles.

'Tama's the fool if she favours Comma over me,' he said.

The children of Boitai came dancing out of the town to meet us, a throng of clamouring, naked, adorable imps. They threw the planes of their bodies into angular contortions as they danced, the shelf of the buttocks out, arms and knees sharply bent, like the stick-dolls carved in wood to house the spirits of ancestral dead. Their skins were glossy and smooth;

these were the little 'mosquitoes', the uninitiated, and therefore unmarked by scarification. Zabogi swung two of them
on each of his brawny arms while they shrieked with glee.

'Oh, Ma!' Zabogi looked ready to burst. 'Here we are,
Hecuba! We're here, we're home!'

Surprisingly perhaps, I too experienced a tingle of reception,
a feeling of arrival at a right place. I realized of a sudden that
I had not been tugged at by purely personal stresses since I
left the plantation. I had been floated in their group buoyancy
of spirit. Never before had I been a part of a unit of people in
this same way. Always I had felt myself the separate one,
unable to share in more than a tangential way in the pooled
enthusiasms of a group. I had made some really serious tries
at it, trying to get off the fringe edge of things, to get lost in
the central whirl. Nothing had ever come of it except a feeling
of spiritual exhaustion and defeat. Now, I had experienced
commonness with people who on the surface of it might
seem to have little in common with myself. This immersion
into their collective humanness was a spiritual invigoration;
it had a deep significance to me.

As I puzzled over it those last few moments of our trek, it
seemed to me it had come about because they had allowed
me to share in the lively relish they felt for themselves.

'I like me plenty the way I am,' Johnny had told me once.
This was not conceit; it was not smug. It was just a decent
self-affirmation with a contagious joyousness about it.

They take some getting used to – people who are contented
and satisfied with what they are and what they have. Our
United States training is to take a dim view of self-satisfaction,
stumbling-block to 'improvement'. I had come to Africa
cumbered with the idea that there is a subtle affinity between
quantity of plumbing and quality of life. It was a distinct
shock in the beginning, to see so much evidence all around
me to the contrary. If there is any relationship between
standard of living and level of happiness, it seemed inversely

proportional. The laughter around a plantation house is likely to come from under it, where the servants live.

They had offered their pride and their laughter, the only wealth they possess, for me to sample and share. These were the invisible bonds which forged us into a tribe on the trek. I did not expect our compactness to hold. We were about to cross the waterside into Boitai, where the Poro would reclaim its sons. If Lega the blacksmith, master of the Poro, chose to be hostile, I was prepared to be singled out along with Comma.

The adults of the town, which is to say all the cult initiates, did not dance out to meet us. They waited on the rise of land above the waterside, chanting their welcome. The women had *shake-shakes* in their hands, gourds strung in beaded cradles of string which are jerked to produce a clacking sound. There was a drum to underscore the rhythm for the gourds. It rolled with sober majesty in a pattern which vaguely re-called the 'March of Priests' (imprinted in memory when I moved down the aisle toward my college diploma). The carriers moved with the pattern. I do not believe an African pair of feet has it in them to contradict a drum! In our slowed and solemn approach, it seemed that the joy of the moment of meeting was so intense, they were purposely prolonging the ecstasy.

As we came closer the drum was muffled and the surge of the women's song swelled in our ears. There was shimmering joy in it, but a great sadness, and a longing, too. I was eager to discover whether I was exaggerating the mood of words which I did not understand, so at the first opportunity after-wards, I asked Zabogi for a translation. I wrote it down as he gave it to me:

> *When a son leaves our womb*
> *We are big with glad;*
> *The glad is our healing.*
> *When he leaves our larger womb,*
> *The village, we lie torn, bleeding.*

There is no healing, no healing
Until a son returns to ourselves,
There is no healing! Only in return
There is healing. Aye, yah, *our sons!*
Stay with us now until we have our
Together in the town of the Deads!

Until the song was done, Zabogi stood in the stream, his face raised and attentive to the massed chorus above us. Our caravan stalled behind him, all of us listening as the feeling of the song flowed down over us. In those moments I unlearned the fallacy that sorrow lies opposite joy. I had heard sorrow and joy merged and transmuted into something larger than either. In reunion, the sadness of separation was not denied but was suffered again to enlarge the happiness of being together at last. I think we lack words in our language to express this union of opposites. The best we can do is to use a hyphen between such words as bitter-sweet or sweet-sour, but all we get is the implication of something which savours of each. That hyphen keeps contraries opposed. The African, although he too lacks the vocabulary to explain a fusion of sorrow with joy, understands perfectly how to accept both in all their devastating force and integrate them.

The crowd stirred and the drum began loud and quick with evenly spaced beats, like a racing heart. Still Zabogi waited, taking in almost individually the crowd above us, turning his head from side to side, sweeping them all. I scanned them carefully, trying to single out three people – Bola the mother, Lega the blacksmith, and Falali the chief.

It was easy to spot the chief. He was in the centre fore-front, seated on a low support which his portly figure completely overflowed. His burnoose of blue and white country-cloth swept out around him in studied folds as though it had been carefully arranged for effect, like a bride's train. The top of his close-cropped grey hair was waist-level with a solid backdrop of women, their hips wrapped in *lappas* of every imaginable dazzling hue. It would have been a blinding stab of colour, barbaric, without the absorbing and blending power of black in the bare chests and arms above it.

As head wife of the chief, Bola's rightful place would be directly behind him. The figure who stood there had a queenly lift to her rather large head, and all I could see of her was moulded in sleek curves. Her breasts were two bountiful cylinders, the tips hanging to her waist. The chief inclined his head slightly back against her as though leaning on the source of his comfort and strength.

I expected Zabogi to rush ahead then to embrace them. Instead he turned back to me and scooped me up in his arms.

'Hang on, Ma,' he yelled. 'I'm taking you *home!*' He galloped through the stream like a wild horse and charged up the slippery clay bank. Bola stepped forward to meet us and he dumped me into the waiting circle of her arms.

'I give you my mother,' he panted. 'My mother, Bola.'

I beckoned Zabogi into the circle. Comma, too, was standing there in a moment. She tried to stretch her arms around all three of us while her tears splashed us. Comma was blinking and trembling. Zabogi wept as copiously and unashamedly as his mother.

Zabogi and Comma both laid their cheeks against their mother's breasts, acknowledgment of her mother-ness, thanksgiving for it. Tribes-people do not kiss on the lips. They say. 'Only chimpanzees and white people do that nasty thing.' The expression of disgust that accompanies this remark suggests that they rate kissing with some of a chimp's other more revolting habits.

Falali, the chief, sat back smiling until Bola had her moment, not imposing himself on the scene, but just happily watching as though he were so addicted to contentment that he could find it even in waiting. He appeared much as Zabogi would eventually, I thought, when Zabogi had learned to give top

priority to laughter, and let serious things straighten themselves without any spluttering attention. The chief's eyes were
the colour of tobacco-stain like Zabogi's, but instead of being
over-solemn and protruding, they were sheltered under a
splendid brow and they fairly crackled with sly merriment.

Zabogi cupped his hand under my elbow to gravely escort
me from his mother to his father. When we stood before
Falali, Zabogi dipped his big frame as though to re-establish
himself on the paternal knee. Had the gesture been carried
through, there would certainly have been need for a new
chief-stool in Boitai! Falali was all outgoing friendliness as
Zabogi translated the customary polite phrases. Creases of the
chief's neck and double chins were new-moon echoes of his
generous up-curved lips. He smiled and smiled at both of us,
not needing to speak often because he said so much with that
welcoming smile.

I thought it a happy circumstance that Comma did not
follow when Zabogi propelled me toward the tree-stump
where Lega, the blacksmith, was a mounted observer. I had
no connection with any mission, of course, but that was a
distinction I could hardly expect Lega to make. A typical
hinterlander, if asked the purpose of a Christian mission, will
answer 'to make us take on white ways'. The medical missions
are exempt from this estimate; they are 'to heal our hurts'.

Lega was agile-looking, close-knit, and he was entirely
naked except for a negligible loin apron the colour of bark.
His nudeness was a large part of the impression of elegant
detachment. Our arrival, so momentous to the others that
they had decked themselves out in their gayest, was apparently
of so little import to him that he felt no need to dress at all.
In that light, a reddish cast of late afternoon gloam penetrating
through fog, he was bronze-brown and lustred like a Malvina
Hoffman sculpture of a smoothly muscled native type. There
are some Negroes who in spite of pigmented skins give the
impression of reflecting light like a sheet of burnished metal.

Lega was one of these. Highlights glinted off the rims of his arms as he stepped nimbly down from the stump.

The African greeting is the beginning of a handshake, a clasp, then, as the palms slide back away from each other, the middle fingers lock and snap. The number of joint-rattling snaps indicates the degree of mutual enthusiasm at the encounter. I did not stretch out my hand to Lega; I sensed him all retracted from me. He had rejected my hand before it was offered. One can't call this sort of thing mind-reading or give it any convincing name at all, but you know what has happened as distinctly as though your thoughts and the other person's had been tape-recorded and played back to you.

I believe that after that first moment he disliked me less than he had planned. I liked him quite a lot more than I expected.

I was quite sure that Lega would not want to be addressed, that his rigid abstinence from petty affairs precluded trivial exchanges with a visitor. Hospitality is the job of the chief. There is a gesture in Africa which is almost a curtsy, although it is only a slight flexing of the knees and a bob of the head. It means, 'I make myself your stranger.' It implies more than guest-status. There is in it something of 'Here I am, not of your people, therefore at your mercy. What comes of it is up to you.'

I said only my name (not to do so is an unforgivable rudeness) and made myself Lega's stranger. He could have cowed me with one piercing glance, but he did not. There was a searching quality in his concentrated study of my face. Lega was no churl. He had a sensitive, one might almost say spiritual face. I looked straight back at him, letting him read of me what he could. At last, he released me with a curt nod.

'Whew!' Zabogi mopped his face and sighed his relief as we walked back to Bola. 'You carried that all right, Ma!'

They had a house ready for me. I asked Zabogi to hustle me to it so they could be done with ceremony and each family have its sons to themselves. On the way we met Comma grimly propelling himself toward the stump where Lega was now seated. As Comma passed me, he paused a moment and his hand went out toward me in a groping, indecisive gesture as though to clutch a strand of my cascading hair. It was exactly the gesture I have seen a frustrated child make toward an anxious mother. Then he caught himself, withdrew his hand, and rubbed the markings on his arm as though they itched, and resolutely went on towards his father. I turned to watch, did not budge, until I saw Lega move over to make room for his son.

'Man, oh! Look at that.' Whenever Zabogi was amazed at anything, his voice dropped to a husky whisper. He always seemed a little reverent of anything that could surprise him. 'Father-ness has sat down on Lega, the blacksmith!'

'Just now do you think?'

Zabogi scratched his left ear, crooking his right elbow in a triangle over his head, this reaching-scratch being a thought-accelerant.

'Nope, Ma. I believe father-ness started to sit down in Lega's heart the day we hid and watched Comma hold still for the fire to burn his marks. Lega learned that day that his son had iron in him. But I doubt whether Lega decided before today to try to hammer that iron into a proper man. It will take some doing, I tell you!'

'What do you mean by that?' My voice was sharper than I intended.

'Oh, Ma, don't always bite at what I say,' Zabogi pleaded. 'What I mean is this: When Lega wants to make something, say a brass anklet, he gets him a hunk of brass, anything with brass in it. Well, he can't just melt a big old hunk. Before the brass will melt, he has got to sit all day, every day, for a long time to scrape and file it into little shavings. After that, it will melt and he can pour it in any shape he wants. Comma is a big old hunk in the awkward shape of a black man with white thinks in his head, the most awkward shape there is. What I mean to say is that Lega will have to sit all day and every day, and Comma will have to hold still for a lot of filing if he is to get fashioned into a proper Loma.'

We saw Lega drop his hand over Comma's shoulder. 'It's all right, Ma,' Zabogi said. 'Come on, here is your house.'

Zabogi flung the door wide and we stepped inside on the red-gold square of light which fell on the dim floor like a welcome mat. Something long and black slithered across the patch of gold.

'It's a snake!' Pointless yelp. In retreat I collided with Zabogi's burly frame.

'Sure it's a snake,' he beamed. 'He is Bola's pet snake. It was on the talking-drums that you don't like rats. This fellow can catch rats past all. Bola wouldn't give him up for just anybody.'

'Thank you, thank Bola, too.' My voice shook and I bit my tongue between chattering teeth. 'If we just put the snake in something, say in a basket, wouldn't the rats fear to come in?'

'Snakes don't like baskets. If you want this snake to stand behind you [defend you], you got to give him his likes.'

'Wh-what does he like?'

'What he likes best is to sleep in people's nice warm beds. Snakes get terrible cold on account of how thin God makes them.'

'I kind of like rats, Zabogi. Come to think of it, rats are real nice little animals.'

The snake lay motionless almost across our feet. It had its head raised as though it were listening. Zabogi had one arm clamped around my shoulders; he wasn't going to let me escape until I properly appreciated this special creature. He put out his other arm toward the reptile and it wound itself around him like an enormous armlet. Its eyes came level with mine, bead-bright and, I thought, hostile.

'You must never squeeze a snake, Ma. Just pick him up easy-like. See?'

'I wasn't going to squeeze it,' I assured him.

Johnny, come to find me, took the situation immediately in hand.

'Zabogi, man,' he said, 'take that damned snake out of here, one time. I don't favour snakes. They make me feel all squiggly.'

Zabogi walked away, stroking the black coils tenderly, soothing away the hurt of our harsh words.

'Ma,' Johnny suggested, 'you better let me dress the bed. For true, you look a little shook!'

X

THORNS ALSO AND THISTLES

You do not look up nor down on a friend,
you look straight across at him.

THE HOUSE they gave me was so new the thatch smelled like damp hay. The door, a single slab cut from the buttress root of a bombox tree, had been intricately carved in bas-relief. The forward surfaces were stained with turmeric, the wood showing through the golden dye in silvery streaks. The recessed areas were charcoal black.

Everything about the house evidenced skill and care. I had long ago succumbed to the charm of a clean mud house; this was the nicest I had ever seen. The bed which Johnny was preparing to 'dress' was a raised clay slab about twelve inches above the floor. The head and foot were high clay partitions, back of which dry firewood was neatly corded. Both bed and floor were carpeted with new pandanus mats the colour of ripe wheat.

In the centre of the floor was a raised cube of clay on which a little fire had burned down to rubescent twinklings. Above the fire, supported on a three-legged black iron ring, was an egg-shaped pottery jar which contained my heated bathwater. There was nothing else in the room except my cases, which seemed in these surroundings a clutter amongst perfection.

Johnny whipped a clean sheet out of a tin trunk. He glowered at the bed, scowled at the sheet.

'You are long past this bed,' he announced. 'A long woman in a short bed! That will be awkward past all!'

146

'I could sleep in my hammock. I am used to that now.'

He was cross with me for thinking of it.

'Hammock is what you have for taboo. Remember? A person should remember his taboo. Else all is trouble.'

'A person should remember short beds before he tells big tales.' I was a little cross myself. In order to give validity to the yarn he had told about my grandmother, he expected me to try to wad myself into that bed.

'The carriers all know that I slept on a hammock on the trail,' I argued.

'The men will stand behind my story. You have got to stand behind me also, Mommio! You see, tonight, when the carriers give the journey to their people, I am to tell how the monkeys dumped your grandmother on the floor!'

It is of no use to try to correct an impression once it has become tribal currency. The monkeys who came out of the jungle surrounding Laurel, Iowa, will live in Lomaland as long as I am remembered in Boitai.

Johnny tried to budge the clay slabs at the ends of the bed. They were as unyielding as though they had been constructed of steel-reinforced concrete.

'Take your measure on the bed, Mommio. Maybe it is longer than it looks.'

It wasn't.

'I don't see why God didn't make everybody to grow up to be the same size,' he grumbled. 'Then, everything would fit everybody. Think of the hellova palaver that would save.'

'If you had not stretched the truth, we wouldn't have to try to stretch the bed,' I pointed out. I was sure that if I insisted on sleeping in the hammock, he would 'forget' to secure one end. Trouble is supposed to follow a broken taboo. There would be a measure of poetic justice in helping trouble along.

'I have it! Try the bed on the bias.'

He was proud that he had mastered that word 'bias'. It had

been hard for him to pronounce back in the days when pidgin was thick on his tongue. After he learned to say it, he wanted all sorts of things 'on the bias' just so he could use the phrase.

The bed was about thirty inches wide at the head and foot, wider in the middle where it adjoined the curving wall of the house. If I lay on my left side with my back to the wall and curved around with it, I could get both head and feet on the slab. I gave in. After all, people do have to stand behind one another. Besides, those tight-drawn sheets looked most inviting. Bedding on a hammock has a way of sliding into a bundle across your middle.

'The shortest distance between two points is a straight line, Johnny. We call that geometry.'

I was silly-tired, this struck me as somewhat humorous. Question (crisp pedantic voice of my old geometry teacher): 'By what means is this hypothesis verified into theorem?' Answer (weary wilted sigh): 'When confronted with a bed which will not comprise the extremities.'

'The shortest distance between your head and your feet is too plenty long, no matter how you bend it! You're tired, Mommio. Take your old geometrys to bed.'

I was scarcely between those crisp sheets, had just started to doze, when Zabogi bustled in to brief me on the evening schedule. He was to M.C. an assemblage in the market compound at which each of us was to give a scrap of the journey. Johnny had top billing. He was to lead off with the tale about my taboo as a sort of preface to my story. Zabogi wanted to 'give' them my people, especially the grandmother. After each of us had made his contribution to the hilarity, a country devil (not to be confused with the sacred Big Devil of the Poro) would come to dance for us.

These country devils are masked entertainers who often dance on concealed stilts. I have seen them enter a compound, standing as tall as the crest of thatch atop a mud hut (twelve or fifteen feet). In the instant it takes to slap a mosquito or bat

F

one's eyes, they would be the height of a doorway, and seemed never to have missed a beat of the drum-pounded rhythm. They are so spectacular they have to be seen in action to be believed.

Zabogi told me that people were already cooking chop in order to have a long night for the fun, 'fine past all'. He implied that instead of taking a nap I had better be polishing up my story.

'The people have heard that you can take anybody any-where, take them a fine long ride on the tip of your tongue,' he said.

Life can get terribly strenuous trying to fit the reputation an African makes for you. I sat up and started to plan my story.

One of the things I carried to Africa was a remarkable letter which my grandmother, Cathran Sietmann, wrote for me to read on the ship. It had not been marred in any parts by the 'forgets'. In it she told how her parents had started to the United States when she was four years old, how she and her sisters had been boarded up in a bunk on the long sea journey, a bunk so cramped that they were unable to walk at first when they were finally set down on American soil. She told what it was like when Iowa was an unfenced prairie, the snow swirling ahead of the plains-swept wind into the cracks of the box-car which was their first home. Then she told what she had learned during a long useful life are the things which help make 'a new song in a strange land'.

I thought this story would hold their interest, and that through it I might be able to 'take them on my tongue' to the United States. I was confident that in spite of losses in translation, I could make them see my country because I would be showing it to them in the person of that frightened little immigrant girl who grew up making a strange life into a splendid new song.

I had noted early in Africa that we do not make friends for

the United States by telling about the things in which we glory – our cities, our highways, our high standard of living, our technical achievements. The tribesman is either bored with these, or annoyed. (Medical facilities are the only part of all this which he covets for his own people.)

But if you mention instead some struggle you have been through, some difficult time, he wants to know every detail. 'I was going to a big school to try to get learning. Hard times sat down on the land (it was 1929). I had no money for chop. No one would give me work. I went from house to house asking. I thought I would have to give up, go back to my family's farm, do without the learning I wanted. . . .'

Immediately, the listener's mouth is agape, his eyes shining with interest. 'Oh, Ma! What then? What then? What did you do? Did you have to eat pepper to fool your belly? To make it think it was full when it was only hot?'

He does not understand your desire to get learning, but he does understand hunger and if hunger was part of the price, he knows it was a matter of importance.

When the first airplane sat down at Roberts' Field, I took the houseboys to see it. They were not impressed. 'It's a hellova big bird, all right,' Johnny said. 'But, Ma, *it can't sing!*'

The people of Boitai would not have wanted to hear about two-car families or automatic washing machines, but I knew they would shelter in their hearts forever a little girl with aching legs.

No rain was falling as we gathered in the market-place, but lightning played over the tree-tops on the hills beyond the town. There were beautifully carved stools for Falali, Bola, Zabogi and myself. Lega was not present. The rumtytoo of the tribe were not allowed stools, they sat on mats on the earth, facing us. Johnny was at my knee, bright and pert as a rice bird in his golden suit. A bonfire behind us lighted the expectant faces of the buzzing crowd. A hush settled over them as Zabogi stood up. In that pause we heard a woman's screams.

The screams were repeated, became more piercing. Zabogi had to hesitate for each one in order to be heard.

'A baby is trying to get itself born,' Zabogi leaned over and whispered to me during one of the enforced breaks in his narrative. 'What a time to do it!'

The crowd shifted uneasily, dividing their attention between Zabogi and the distraction.

'Get Tama to take me to the woman,' I told him. Bola followed us.

The old women in the hut wouldn't let me come in because I was clothed, midwives must work nude. Birth is too sacred to be profaned with clothes-pride. They did allow me to stand just inside the door. The girl in labour was a young little creature; I could make out her features vaguely by the light of a burned-down fire. Tama told me this was the girl's first pregnancy and that she had been in labour a long time. She lay on the floor on her back, writhing in agony. Several very old women stood over her, each holding a long flexible bamboo in her hand.

'The *pickin* don't agree to leave the mother,' Tama explained. 'They beat the woman's belly to make the *pickin* change its mind.'

'Tell them to put up those bamboos!' I said. 'Run, get two of my lanterns. Fetch the boiled water on the hearth and a bar of my soap. Get some man to help you carry. Then, hurry back so you can Loma my English. Hurry!'

I had twice assisted at births, in a minor role, when I worked in the West Virginia hill-country, but I don't know much midwifery. However, I thought almost any assistance, or even none at all, would be preferable to the attention she was receiving.

They would not allow a man to approach within yards of the place, so Tama and I lugged in everything ourselves. The old women just stared when Tama relayed my order for them to put up their rods, but they obeyed. The girls' screams had become exhausted squawks, and finally just gurglings in her throat. The women were frightened enough of the situation then to let me approach. The feeble lanterns were not of much use except to make me realize how dark it was in the hut.

The old women gathered around the girl in a tight ring while I scrubbed my hands and arms. It was suffocating in the room and I wanted them to open the door and stand back away from her, but Tama would not even ask them to do that.

'They are begging her to confess,' Tama explained. 'A baby won't come into a wrong-place. If she was frisky with some man not her husband, or if she had had bad-mouth [quarrels] with her husband, the *pickin* won't agree to come to that kind of people. If she will confess, then the old women will go tell Falali [the girl was one of the chief's younger wives]. Then Falali will come and stand outside the door and beg the child to forgive all the badness that has been done, and the *pickin* will come, one time.'

The girl was in so much pain that I doubt whether she heard them begging her to confess. They gave her a twig to clench her teeth into. Blood trickled from her lips, she had been brave, had tried to stifle her screams.

'What are they doing now, Tama?' Bola was kneeling between the girl's legs, a razor on the earth floor beside her. Two old women knelt at the girl's head.

'The baby is starting to leave,' Tama said. 'They are sprinkling pepper in the woman's nose to make her sneeze That will bring the baby for sure, now.'

The girl did not sneeze. She was dead. I was sure of it even before I felt for her pulse. When Bola stood up, she had the baby by the heels. She smacked him soundly and he let out a lusty squall.

I cannot say that the girl died because of the inelastic scar tissue which had formed after the ritual circumcision in the

Sande, but this must certainly have added to the difficulty of her labour. Tama told me that when the girl was in the Sande, she had 'lacked small to die' of fear when she saw the *Zo* approaching with the razor (some of the girls do die of fear) and because of the fear, she had struggled. This resulted in awkward surgery and accounted for the excess of 'dead part' (scar tissue).

We wrapped the girl's body in a white country-cloth and lifted her on to the clay bed-slab. The old women tucked the ends of the cloth gently around the small bare feet, patted the abused abdomen they had so recently felt they must flog. Tears streamed down their wrinkled old faces and they clutched at one another for comfort. How many times they must have seen this scene re-enacted, they who were fortunate enough to have survived it themselves.

The fumes of sloshed kerosene mingled in the closed room with the reek of blood and sweat. The nausea which welled over me was partly from these, but mostly, I think, from the rage I felt against the needlessness of this death, and my own impotence to avert it.

The thought which rose to torment me: Suppose that Comma went on with his training. Could he in time to come, when Zabogi would be chief, prevent such disasters as the one I had just witnessed? The answer to that is beyond knowing; the question still disturbs my sleep. There are many possibilities. The one in which I find some fragment of relief for my own responsibility is that Comma himself would probably not have survived, had the matter been put to test. When Zabogi's son is chief, perhaps, and Comma's children will have no need to burn the marks of their learning into their flesh with fire. . . .

The question would seem so much simpler if one had never been near it. Africa needs doctors, why not train Africans in medicine? They need milk, why not teach them to milk their goats? They lack vitamins, why don't they eat the abundant fruit? Like so many questions for which the answers seem simple and obvious, these questions leave out the attitudes and biases of the people who must make the answers.

If a mother believes that goats' milk will make her child grow into a bleating, stupid, head-butting oaf, there is no use to talk about the nutritive value of goat-milk. It is not possible to change her idea unless one could uproot the whole idea, so deeply imbedded in African thinking, of the *essence* of all things, animate and inanimate, a fear not likely to be accomplished in our time. The nutritionists might better talk to the wind; the wind would not respond with enmity.

If people believe that the cure for disease lies in some magical formula taught in the Sande and the Poro, an African educated in 'white' medicine would find himself without patients. When a white doctor brings 'white medicine', that is a different matter. He has behind him *his* old ones from ancient times; his authority and skill come from them.

I left the moaning old women in the hut and walked back to my house thinking of the immensity of this problem, this incident in Boitai multiplied by most of Africa. Not one person was abroad in the village. Lightning still ran on the hills around the town, flickering eerie lights over the empty compound, like a flashing green neon above a deserted street.

I was glad to find Johnny in my house, building up the fire.

'Could you brew me up a cup of tea, Johnny? I feel sick.'

'It's all ready,' he said. 'I knew you would need it.'

'I thought you were going to sleep in the chief's house with Zabogi, Johnny.'

'Not tonight!' He shook his head. 'Just before the sun gets up, the women of the town will hold a Cursing of Men. If they catch one, they will lack small to beat him to death. I sleep on your floor tonight, Mommio. Please? It is the women's – what do you call it when people try to get even?'

'Revenge?'

'That's it. The women will take revenge because it is
woman that has hurt and dies from a *pickin*.'

The women did not hold off until dawn for their cursing.
We soon heard them, whacking on doors with clubs, shouting in the hoarse and helpless voices of anger.

Then we heard a surprised yelp that did not come from a
woman's throat. It was distinctly male, and something about
the timbre of the voice was familiar.

'Johnny, that sounds like Comma.' We listened, heard it
again.

'It is Comma, Mommio. He told me that when the cursing
reached his door, he was going to open right up, stand in the
doorway, and give pause to the women. He said he was going
to explain to them that it is not the fault of men that women
have terrible bad hurts when a *pickin* leaves them. He said
that God ordered it so because a long time since, a white
woman named Eve ate something taboo. Isn't that stupid past
all? Comma said Eve's husband caught trouble, too, on
account of it. God told the husband. "Thorns also and thistles
shall make your face sweat." I told Comma that everytime
is not the time to tell a story, but you know Comma! He has
got to learn all things the hard way. He always stands under
a dead limb.' (Invites trouble, is accident prone).

We heard it again, over and over, rising above the thuds
of the clubs and the frenzied chant of the women – a boy's
voice trying to ward off what protesting reason could not.

Johnny, understandably, would not follow me across the
compound to the source of the din. When I reached Comma,
he lay alone in the dust where he had fallen. The women
had advanced in full force on another house.

Comma was quite conscious when I knelt beside him, and
amazingly cheerful. There were some nasty welts on his head,
but no bones seemed to be broken. He had been beaten up
about as thoroughly as the day when he returned from Lomaland, saying he had been attacked and robbed of the chimpan-

zee he had purchased. He smiled up at me as though his misery were in some way delicious. There was something perverse and rather horrible about his delight in this pain.

'Shall I bring you some aspirin?'

'Oh, no, please! I want to feel this headache. You see, when women hold a Cursing of Men, they do not beat boys and nobodies. They reckoned me a man! And to be reckoned a man by the women of Boitai is a fine large something!'

'You'll have some fine large somethings on your head by morning! There must be a more comfortable way to get yourself reckoned a man!'

'Anything is something! There is no easy way to get counted a man among Lomas.'

To prove himself nothing other than one more man of Boitai, he had deliberately put himself in line for a flogging. When we left the plantation, his hopes had seemed wholly centred on his mission-born dream. In seven days that too large ambition had dwindled until he was willing to settle for only this, the too little.

'Did you really think you could reason that mob away, Comma?'

'No, I didn't,' he admitted. 'But I thought it would be interesting to measure my speech against their vex. Failing that, to let them take measure of me. If they had spit in the dust and failed to beat me for a man, how could I have faced my father again?'

'Why didn't your father hold you from coming out here? You are staying with Lega, aren't you?'

'Well, my father did advise against it.'

He dwelt on 'father', broke it into syllables. His tongue held on to the word, caressed it.

'Well, you should have listened to him.'

'After I told my father my plan to try to reason with the women, my father said, "Son, I can throw you plenty of sense about many things. But about women, no man can tell

F•

another anything at all. The Tolds won't reach. Every man has got to learn about women for his own self." Well, tonight I learned not to try to reason with women! Women are man's *thorns also and thistles* ever since Eve ate the butter-pear.'

A Sunday sort of hush hung over the village the morning after the death and the cursing. Women going to the water-side to bring back water in the pottery jars balanced on their heads walked slowly with a subdued mien. Their fury at pain and death had been spent; they were again ready to meekly accept the endless chores attendant to living.

Bola sat by the body of the dead girl, fanning a palm leaf over the still form. Throughout the morning, people came and went, bringing gifts of cola nuts. Bola would press these against the girl's palms, repeat the messages given with them. Bola's repetitions in a louder voice was the only outward concession they made to the fact that she no longer breathed.

As Tama translated them to me, they were well-wishings for the journey to the spirit world. 'May you walk well.' 'May no bad palaver catch you on the way.' 'Our hearts go with you to all who have gone before.' 'We will care well for your child. We beg you, do not call the child to be with you in the village of the Deads.'

'What will you send with her?' Tama asked me. They had already asked me for a bar of my 'sweet-soap' to bathe her.

'What do you think she would like?'

Tama did not hesitate. 'Your sweet scent, the one you put on us outside Boitai.'

There were only a few drops left.

'Send the bottle with her,' Tama said. 'That will give her a fine thing to show in Deads' Town. They will all crowd around her and she will tell them a white woman wanted to help her.'

Of all the things I had with me (many in comparison to their meagre possessions), any one of which I would have given them for her grave, had they asked me, what they coveted most was an almost empty phial of fragrance. That little touch of feminine vanity which they assumed for her allied me to those women as much as my compassion for the suffering which is so large a part of their lives.

The old women in the hut exclaimed over the glass bottle, fondled it, held it to the light, demanded to know 'what it said'. They cannot imagine form without symbolic meaning. Their commonest spoons, their most ordinary utensils are pregnant with implications. A long ground-glass stopper fitted into the flared neck of the bottle. They thought this must be phallic, a symbol of conception. I shook my head. The bottle was hand-blown crystal, less machined than most of our articles of use, but I could not claim for it this deeper meaning.

'But it is womb-shaped,' Bola argued through Tama.

This amazed me. 'How does she know that shape?'

'Oh, we know it well,' Tama said. 'If the baby had also died and not been born, they would have cut it from the woman's side and buried it in a little grave of its own. These old women have had to do that many times. They know how a woman is fashioned. A person does not forget learning that has been wet down with tears.'

Tears! That gave her another clue to a possible meaning for the bottle. She and Bola discussed it at length. Bola was obviously deeply stirred as she instructed Tama in what she must tell me: 'A black woman's tears are so many, they have to be small. Troubles are so plenty, death is so often, there are not enough tears to cover all the sorrow. When a white woman gives a tear for a black one, that is seldom, almost to never. We hold a tear from you. The sun will not dry it away. It will not leak from us between our fingers.'

What I gave them was an impersonal trinket; what they received from me was a token of myself. Such is the alchemy of love.

I nodded. This meaning I was willing for them to assume. They came to me, one by one, wanting to stroke my palms, first with the palm of my right hand up and the left one down, then again, reversed. They were stroking themselves into me, myself into them.

Even now, with years and miles between us, I can recall those old faces in the hut that morning more clearly than though I were studying photographs of them. Every seam and wrinkle and flicker of expression testifies to their open goodness, their wisdom for living, their capacity for love, and best of all their self-respect. It was their self-respect which enabled us to meet as equals in spite of my abundance of possessions and poverty of experience.

With a few certain native people, especially with the old women, I have sometimes felt a rare intimacy, as though some bond of spirit united us immediately with an almost mystic affinity. We had no words of common language, yet we felt much which did not need to be spoken, much which was so delicate it might easily have been shattered by speech. We communicated to each other what we were without any pretence, we revealed ourselves without apology. This intimacy we shared is one I have seldom experienced with people whose skin matches my own. Before whom of my friends dare I stand without any shred of pretence?

Women who die in childbirth are buried in a separate graveyard which men may not enter. These old women had dug the grave early in the morning. The only ceremony which might be called a burial service was held in the market compound. Falali, himself, asked me to speak at this gathering. I worried about whether Lega had given his approval to the arrangement. Both as the chief and the husband, Falali would seem to have the right to arrange whatever kind of ceremony he wished. But in tribal society, even death is a communal event. That would give Lega as the spiritual head of the community, an interest in what was permitted. Further, I was at a complete loss to know what to say. I knew it would be an affront to offer a prayer. Only the old mothers would be thought worthy to do that; I was not only young, but also childless. I had minutes to decide what to do, the body had been wrapped in mats, ready to be carried from the hut.

Tribesmen frequently charge that whites are lacking in a sense of reverence and wonder. Uneasily, I thought about this, and it gave me the clue about what to say. In a few words and very simply so that Zabogi could find Loma words into which to fit it, I told them the Christmas story. I said that any birth is a miracle-thing, whether it is a young rice plant bursting out of the seed rice, or a fawn just getting its shaky legs under it after being dropped by a doe, or a human child coming to live among people. Tribal people feel the mystery of birth deeply themselves and my audience nodded and assented.

Then I said that my people celebrated one birth in particular above all others, that there was no need of a cargo of fine things to set it apart, a stable was purposely the scene. I thought that the stable had walls of rock and an earth floor. Tribal babies must be born on the earth, in contact with the sacred 'Great Mother'. My listeners liked the idea of white people accepting as special a baby born on the earth. I said that the meaning of this Christmas birth was love and good-will among all people, and that whenever men feel and live out goodwill toward one another, that is again a star-brightening thing.

Comma scowled as I spoke. I am sure that he did not think what I said was scripturally accurate. Lega watched me between narrowed lids. His face registered neither approval nor disapproval; it was mask-like, enigmatic. I believe he only half heard the words. His attention was centred on me, did not shift to Zabogi to pick up each translated sentence. He was interested, not in the words I was giving, but in what I was giving of myself as a human being. If I had felt the slightest arrogance, either in myself or in my religion, Lega would have been the first to know it and resent it. A white person does not need to be insolent to make enemies for his race. If he treasures a secret thought that he is in any way superior to a black man, even though he never breathes this secret, it will be known. One many sincerely believe that all men are his brothers, but if he feels it is his 'bounden duty to enlighten these brethren' with a religion he considers superior, he will find his sense of brotherhood a lost achievement.

No one can be friends with another unless there is a feeling of equality between them. The deficiencies and abundances in the spirit of each must add up to a similar total. 'You do not look up or down on a friend; you look straight across at him.' If I were ever to be friends with Lega it was necessary that he take this careful measure of me. His scrutiny was more encouraging than the less critical approval of the others.

When I finished the few words I had to say, the old women carried the mat-shrouded body to the grave. None of the rest of us went with them. As they returned to their homes they were wailing.

The colas they scattered in the grave must have grown into splendid trees by now. I like to think of them arched over the path that winds past the place where they carried the girl, grown out of the well-wishing seeds they pressed against her palm, and to know that down under the roots is that tear-drop of crystal. This is not a sentimental whimsy. The reason I like to remember it: I learned that day it is among the thorns and thistles of living that we come closest to others. Shared surpluses have fleeting value, are perishable; shared sorrows do not trickle through the fingers nor are they lost to the sun.

XI

SAVOUR OF SALT

An empty rice bag cannot stand up.

THE TAILOR of Boitai sat on the piazza of a house which was even larger than the chief's quarters. He was furiously pedalling a thunderous old Singer, sewing an immense pocket in the centre of a new chief-robe.

'*Boi Ava!* [Friend comes]'. He lifted his bare feet from the treadle and the machine coasted on a bit unheeded, rattling to a convulsive stop. The man's words were friendly but his face was not. It was too crotchety for so young a man and the arrogance in it was not the natural arrogance of youth, it was hard and brittle. Had I been doing a quick sketch of him, I would have indicated his mouth with a thick black line bracketed with parentheses.

'*Yana.*' Zabogi had coached me in the simple words of polite exchange. I nodded briefly. I was headed for a spot outside the village which Zabogi had told me about, a pool of sacred fish overhung with flowers.

The tailor switched to English. 'How do you like my wife?' He nodded toward the machine. The frame was blistered with peeling veneer, the belt had been replaced by a lumpy raw-hide thong, the whole affair was so battered it was hard to believe it could function at all.

'She seems faithful.' I thought it best not to mention the obvious decrepitude. 'How long have you been married?'

He was delighted that I fell in with his fancy.

'Long enough to know all her faults. Also, long enough to

163

have paid all the dowry. She is entirely mine.' He patted the flywheel affectionately.

'Is she quite well?'

'That is the one I wanted to talk.' His voice hushed to a sick room whisper. 'The truth is she is not altogether well. Have you brought any castor oil?'

'Why, yes, I have. But I have better medicine than that – my fine gun oil.'

'Oh, no! Castor oil is the one! Just let me have some of that.'

We cleaned out some lint around the bobbin and fiddled with the tension. He contradicted everything I said about that, readjusted everything I adjusted.

'Look, friend,' I told him, 'I have a Singer, too. You can't argue with me about a sewing-machine. Have you noticed the gold suit that the Bassau boy, Johnny wears? I tailored that!'

'I noticed it had an awkward set to the sleeves,' he said.

The machine was his and I had no right to tamper with it, but my annoyance with him had passed beyond the realms of reasonableness. He kept saying that a woman couldn't possibly know anything about a sewing machine and I kept saying that I was one woman who did. What we were really at odds about was a woman's right to know, not whether I did know, and that was what riled me. That tailor should have read Nietzsche, I thought. He would have revelled in such sentiments as 'in woman there is so much pedantry, super-ficiality, schoolmasterliness, petty presumption. . . .'

I finally decided that I was only demonstrating that Nietzs-che could, on occasion, be applicable. When the tailor had the machine in a final state of imbalance which drew the lower thread tight as a harp-string and the upper one came through in a clutch of matted loops, I stopped my petty presumption of knowledge.

'You may have a sewing machine,' he said, 'but you aren't

married to yours. Yours is just one more of your many things. Now let me tell you, to marry means to care for. This machine is a person to me. Her name is Kalagi [Moon Halo]. She brings me all the respect I have in this village. To be a tailor is next to being a blacksmith. The only difference is that smithing came from the Old Ones, and tailoring comes from New Ways. A woman cannot even touch the tools of a smith. It ought to be the same way with the tools of a tailor!'

'I'm sorry I humbugged Moon Halo,' I apologized. 'I know that even though machines may be exactly alike when they are new, they change with use, just as people change when they get older.'

I was truly sorry. I realized too late that I had presumed to penetrate a realm which he felt to be his own special, mystic sphere. I had cheapened it, made it common, by claiming to share it. Even though I might know considerable about sewing machines, by insisting on adjusting his, I had thrown something out of kilter between himself and it. Moon Halo would not be quite the same inviolate, adorable creature she had seemed before, not for a while anyway.

I don't think he had entirely forgiven me, but he had something else on his mind.

'I hear you brought a cargo of salt.' He said this with studied carelessness as though it were intelligence which could scarcely be of interest to anyone, but would do to mention in the way one mentions the weather. Only a brightening in his eyes betrayed the importance of that salt.

There was probably not the smallest item in my cases which was not already known to everyone in the village. Not that they would have rifled through them! What they did do was to persuade Johnny to hold a clandestine 'showing' to a select few back of my house while I still slept. Their comments (Englished by Zabogi for Johnny's benefit) were what had awakened me. My toothbrush: 'What an awkward way to get a clean mouth!' A fuzzed-out stick had all sorts of advantages. A roll of toilet paper: 'Why carry that big stuff? God made trees grow everywhere for the purpose with leaves as soft as velvet *lappa*.' A brassiére: 'What nonsense! How can that nothing of a cloth crush a woman's breasts to make them look *pickin*-used as God intended?'

'Now this thing here,' I heard Johnny explain, 'is a book. For all that it looks like it had been beaten in a mortar and chewed by a chimpanzee and left out all night in the rain, it has got a big man inside it. His name is Ulysses.'

'*Hauh!*' They snorted their unbelief.

'That is the medicine [magic] of a book,' Johnny instructed Zabogi to tell them. 'It is wonderful past all!'

Johnny plumping for literacy? That startled me fully awake.

'Now we got two cases that stay shut until we leave. I can't tell you the fine thing that stays inside.'

'Salt? Not salt?'

'Tell them, Zabogi, I won't say they are right.' Then he laughed to let them know that they were.

I pretended sleep while Johnny smuggled back into my house the treasure he had been displaying. So now, of course, everyone including this scalawag of a tailor knew about that cargo of precious salt.

Salt is a word of deep meaning to a hinterlander. It is scarce and expensive, coming up from the coast or down from the Sahara on men's heads. It is heavy, it dissolves in rain, it crumbles. The Sahara salt is in slabs like bacon which tend to crack and break when stacked one on the other atop a carrier's head.

There is 'country salt', but it has more the characteristics of lye. Canna blossoms and stalks are burned, the ashes leached to make it. A leaf-lined cone of rattan holds the ashes while water filtering through them, drips into a clay receptacle below. After the water is boiled off, a small quantity of bitter grey residue remains in the pot, salt without savour.

When I told my houseboys the story of Lot's wife, they could not understand why being turned into salt was considered a grievous end. When a tribal woman dies, her husband is required to pay a death benefit to her family. A woman turned into a pillar of salt at death would be worth a great deal of money. 'What woman, other than this Lot's wife, was ever worth death benefit and bride-price, all two, after she was dead!'

To think, then, that two crates of real salt were standing unopened in Boitai! The tailor's eyes could not have gleamed with more avarice had the contents been gold.

'I want to buy the salt.' It was more of a command than a request.

'The salt is not for sale. It is for free.'

'I am an educated man,' he boomed. I could not see what his education had to do with our new argument.

'Oh? What did you study?'

'I studied to bargain. Under Baysah of Salala!'

I knew that I was supposed to be as impressed as though someone had told me that he had majored in anthropology under, say, Hooton of Harvard.

'I congratulate you. Baysah has a nose for money.'

'Baysah has a nose for need,' he corrected me. 'I also have the nose. My name is Suo. It means "head". I would rather like it if you cared to address me as The Head. Now, let us speak of need. I need salt. Back of us here in my house is my store, no salt on the shelves. Let me show you my shop.'

'I don't believe that you have anything for sale that I need today.' I was sure he was working up to some fresh unpleasantness.

'That is where you lack the nose! I have some Tolds for sale. My price is salt.'

'I am not selling salt and I am not buying Tolds!'

'The Tolds are concerning Comma.'

He was trying to tease me along with bits and pieces now.

braced myself against his cunning, but I was all ears for any scraps of information he might pass out as free samples.

'I know all that I need to know about the lost money, Suo.'

'You can't possibly know the truth! The truth took place inside my store. It was there that I took the money and put the chimpanzee's hand in Comma's and they started out of Boitai in the night without any torch to light the way.'

This, if it were true, was a large free sample. It checked with what Comma had told me: 'I started out in the night without a torch so none would know. . . .'

'Can you prove that?' I challenged him. I tried to conceal the interest I felt, but I have a give-away face.

'Ah!' He rubbed his long hands together. 'Now, if I can prove it, what about the salt?'

'Absolutely, *no!*' I had to stand firm on that. Tribes-people have no respect whatever for a person who does not stick by the kind of emphatic declarations I had been making. Any-way, what did it matter now? I was quite sure that Comma had taken the money to redeem Bola. I thought he had practically admitted it at the waterside when he talked about his attempt at suicide. Everything about the painful affair had been comfortably resolved in my mind until this Suo the Head reopened all the tantalizing possibilities, unsealed the doubts, made me wretched.

'On the first of December, you owed the Firestone Trading Company twelve pounds six!' If he had been accusing me of murder, he could not have pointed a more incisive finger or put more scorn in his voice.

'Possibly.'

'You wrapped some of the purchase money for the chim-panzee in that bill. That is a terrible wrong-way to treat a bill.'

'The bill had been paid,' I said meekly.

'It should have been paid, *receipted and* filed! Besides that, it was too much to owe. It is more than the price of a woman or a cow, or even a sewing machine.'

The only other person who has ever looked at me with exactly this combination of mingled disgust, pity, and faint hope, was an accountant who tried to teach me the rudiments of book-keeping.

'But now, to get back to the matter in hand,' Suo continued, 'of course, I can offer proof. Also, although I am noted for my head, I have a *stomach!*'

By this, he meant he had honour. The stomach is considered the seat of the conscience. 'When a person feels guilty, his food will refuse to lie down. Old Conscience is kicking it around.'

'This proof? Is it something I can hold in my hands? No, just the spot – "Comma stood there, I stood there, the chimpanzee between us." ' I was certainly getting drawn into this.

'You could hold the proof in your hands if I dug it up. It is sealed under the floor, sealed in concrete.'

Concrete? I thought I had him trapped now.

'Where did you get concrete?'

'From Monrovia. I can show you the receipted bill. Concrete is dear past salt, I tell you. I even had to buy a USA rubber raincoat for it to wear on the trail. You see I am treasurer to Falali. An empty rice bag cannot stand up! [It takes substance, in this case money, to maintain prestige.] The hut-tax money for this village is all down there under my floor sealed in concrete against the day the Government sends a soldier to collect it. Falali does not have a head for money. He has made me his head.'

'I thought it was the pride of the Lomas that their keys need no locks.'

Keys are highly esteemed as symbols of wealth and power. The key-motif is used on textiles, wooden spoons, clay pots. The locks which the keys once fitted seem of little concern. People will buy broken locks if only they have keys.

'Oh, I have to seal the money away from my own self,

he explained. 'You see, I also understand about interest. That is the best feeling there is – to know that money is working instead of myself. You can see how the rice bag would sag to the floor if the village money were all out working and could not be called in when the tax collector showed up. I have to cement the money away from myself so I can not hear it beg me to put it to work.'

'How would I be sure that a chimpanzee was given for some of the money under your floor?'

'The proof of that is wrapped with the money,' he said.

'I might send you a sack of cement when I get back to the coast,' I suggested.

'What proof have I that you would remember to do it?'

'I also have a stomach,' I told him coldly.

'I will have to hang head on it,' he said. 'I will give you my answer after Comma's trial.'

'There isn't going to be any trial, Suo.'

'Hump!' He snorted. 'That trial is as certain as more rain. Word has gone out to all the villages in the clan. The day is set. What you wish, has nothing to do with it, nothing at all.' This seemed a source of great satisfaction to him.

'What day has been set?'

'The third market day. I advised Falali on it. Everyone will come to the first market just to look at you. That's one big market. They will come to the second just to see Tama's beating. That's two big markets. They will come to the third to see the trial. Three big markets!'

Markets are held in Boitai every five days. That gave me about two weeks to try to head off that trial.

'What would you do if you were Comma, Suo? Would you want to stand trial even if no one were accusing you of anything?'

'You have asked the right man,' he beamed. 'I am the NEW AFRICAN! I am first of all, a proper Loma (a Poro initiate). But I am also educated. I have put learning on top of what I am first and always. It is like you eat meat with plenty of salt on it and then take a drink of good water. The salt needs the water and the water needs the salt. Water without the salt is slosh in the insides. That is what Comma has been, a slosh in the belly of his people. What Comma should do, one time, is to get him a white chicken and see whether Lega will take it.'

When a boy wants to become apprenticed to a smith he takes his request in the form of a white chicken and presents it at the smithy. If the smith takes the fowl, he indicates that he is willing. But that does not settle the matter. The smith's tools have to be 'asked' if they will accept the new servant. (The tools are more important than the man, 'they own him, and have in them the medicine of all the Old Ones who ever used them'.) Two cola nuts are split and thrown to get the 'answer' from the sacred tools. If all the faces fall the same way, either up or down, the answer is an enthusiastic acceptance. Three up, lukewarm. Two up, two down, extremely doubtful. If the colas give a favourable reply to the candidate, the fowl is sacrificed to the tools.

'Does Lega have any sons besides Comma, Suo?'

'He has had plenty, plenty, but all have died.'

'Suo, I would like to hold talk with Lega.' It seemed imperative to me to find some way to communicate to Lega that what I wanted for Comma was for him to become a useful member of the tribe. I wanted Lega to know that he did not have to demonstrate his priority to the boy before me.

Suo shook his head. 'That will take some big thinks,' he said. 'It is not easy for a foreigner to reach Lega.'

'Always before, I have been able to make friends with my hands,' I said. 'When Tama tried to put sense in my toes so they would hold the warp for my hands to weave raffia rice bags, that is when we became friends. The wood-carvers in the villages where I have stayed have always matched their calluses with mine, and we started friends right away. The first time my hands have failed me is when I laid them on Moon Halo, just now.'

'That is because tailoring is a business,' Suo said. 'I don't think you have any head for business. As for smithing, that is a religion. You can't reach Lega with your hands. As I have already told you, a woman may not even touch the tools of a smith. You can't make friends by putting your hands on someone's religion.'

'I have a hunk of brass I brought for the blacksmith's *dash*.' I suggested.

Suo shook his head again. 'Don't give it to him until all is finished and you are ready to go home. Lega can not be bought.'

I had already decided that Lega was above price.

'I will try to think of something,' Suo promised.

'Thank you, Suo,' I said. He had started to warm toward me as soon as I asked his advice. He looked almost pleasant as he stuck out his hand to seal the bargain of 'giving me his head'.

'Whether you decide to sell some Tolds for cement, or whether you don't,' I told him, 'I will in any case send you some sewing-machine needles for Moon Halo when I get back to the coast.'

'Oh, don't bother,' he said. 'Lega can make finer ones than you can buy. What I would like, though, is another bottle of castor oil for her.'

'Good day, now, Suo the Head.'

'You forget to bid good day to Moon Halo,' he reproved me.

'Good day, Moon Halo!'

She answered with a snap of threads and fearful clanking deep in her inmost parts, as Suo again set foot to the treadle.

Lega came to my house alone in the night, carrying a burning stick of palm-rib for a torch. When I opened the door, he motioned that I must follow him and be silent. I was afraid to obey him, afraid not to. I made a sort of compromise by following him but not silently. On my way out of the house I purposely bumbled against a half-full kerosene tin, hoping to let others know I was astir. I doubt that anyone heard the racket. African slumber is heavy and deep. The sleepers are so completely relaxed they seem to be drawing in breath through the soles of their feet.

I am sure that Lega knew I was afraid. Whether or not Africans can actually smell fear, in a physical sense, they always seem to be able to recognize its presence. I knew how easy it would be for him to arrange an accident.

'The white woman had to go to the bush to toilet in the night. A cassava snake lay on the dry path, its hinged teeth dripping poison. . . .' Or, 'She did not know where we had the pit to catch leopards, the one with the sharpened iron stakes set in the bottom. . . . None saw it happen. We found her there in the morning.'

I resisted an almost overwhelming desire to strap my revolver on under my coat. If Lega's purposes were benign, this would be an unforgivable thing to do; if they weren't, well, his cunning would be ample to provide a situation where a gun would be of no use.

He put his free hand under my elbow. I felt my arm quiver against his palm. When Zabogi handled me, boosting me up on his shoulders to ride across a swamp, hoisting me bodily over rocks or logs, he always toted me as though I were a valuable cargo, but neuter as a sack of rice. Lega's touch was different. There was something urgent and tense about it.

Lega stopped in front of his house and flung open the door. He pushed me in ahead of him.

I heard Comma before I saw him in the dim light. He was moaning, rolling from side to side, his hands clutched to his abdomen.

Now I understood! The Deads had sent for all of Lega's

other sons. Had they only waited until he opened his heart to this one before they claimed him, too?

My first thought was that Comma might have been injured internally during the beating. His face was feverish, his breath sour. Lega watched my every move, held the torch so he could study my face. Comma would not halt the rhythm of his moaning so I could question him. I had to shake him into quiet.

'Where did the woman's clubs reach you, Comma?'

'Only my head and my shoulders. My insides hurt, it is not from the beating.'

Then he set up his moaning again and I tried to decide what to do. I had to do something, Lega's eyes demanded it. If Comma lived and I had done nothing to help him, Lega would hate me for refusing aid. If Comma died and I had done nothing to prevent it, his hate would be past endurance. I gambled on Comma living, either because of or in spite of some treatment.

'Comma!'

Rocking moan. No answer. More shaking. Some intuition told me that he was suffering more from nervous tension than from his abdomen. He told me later that Lega thought I was shaking an evil spirit out of him. In a way, I was.

'Do you need castor oil, Comma?'

He slowly tallied up days on his fingers. Now that he had something to do, he did not moan at all.

'I sure do!'

I was afraid that Moon Halo had soaked up the last of the castor oil. I indicated to Lega that I would go and return.

I had brought enough medicine on the trip to take a hypochondriac around the world a couple of times. All along the way, the sick of the villages had presented themselves for 'white medicine'. Usually, I gave each one only a salt tablet, after which they probably did feel somewhat better. With pathetic hopefulness they showed me their festering ulcers, their half-faces consumed with yaws, their infected toes from which the jiggers had not been dug out before the egg sac hatched a swarm. Once, even some lepers came out of the bush to beg for aid. They extended their palms from which some of the fingers had rotted away, and all I could lay there were a few aspirin.

There are a few great men of our time, men of the stature of Dr. Albert Schweitzer of Lambaréné and Dr. George Harley of Ganta, who realized before they went to Africa that a cargo of goodwill was not adequate equipment to deal with the problems of a sick continent and they received training in medicine for the purpose of taking these skills to Africa. This part of our civilization the native people are ready and eager to accept. Many of the labourers on the Firestone Plantations told me that the reason they were willing to walk across Liberia, leaving their families and their farms behind, was not to earn money in the rubber, but because Firestone had 'needles for free' (injections against yaws and gonorrhea).

Here I was fumbling around for a bottle of castor oil, so common in the United States that almost anyone can have it, yet so rare and wonderful in Africa that it is precious beyond imagining. I came up, finally, with an unopened bottle.

En route back to Lega's, I stopped at the chief-house and banged on the door. I wanted a witness to what I was going to tell Lega.

It was quite a problem to rouse Zabogi. Falali's quarters were complicated. His house proper was rectangular with a hall running through the centre. The hall led out of a back door into a compound around which the huts of his many wives were clustered, the largest hut being Bola's.

Falali did not come to the door himself. He sent his wife-of-the-night. (A chief does not dare show preference among his women. Those who are not nursing a child or far advanced in pregnancy expect to share the chief-bed in rotation). The woman who answered the door seemed frightened and dazed.

After I repeated Zabogi's name several times, she took me through the hall into the hut-enclosed compound in the back and pointed vaguely at what might have been any one of several huts. Then she fled.

I found Zabogi after waking a number of people in the effort, and he humped along at my heels.

'It's Comma,' I explained. 'He's sick. It's his insides.'

Zabogi was not sympathetic. 'Why can't he let people be until sun-up? He could hold his belly tight.'

'That's not why I called you. I want you to give Lega some Tolds from me.'

'Oh, that's a different palaver,' Zabogi said. 'I will let myself come awake for that. Make go, Ma.'

Comma gulped down the castor oil, most of the bottle, without a grimace.

'Now Zabogi,' I said, 'this is what I want you to tell Lega: the sickness in your son needs the cure he will have when he finds a white chicken and carries it to you at the smithy.'

Amazement spread over Lega's face. He demanded that Zabogi repeat this three separate times. Then his hands shot out toward mine, one of them palm up, one palm down. We suddenly had commonness which he wanted to merge through our palms.

I slept late the next morning. When I looked out Comma was jumping around refereeing a wrestling match between two lively little 'mosquitoes'.

'How do you feel, Comma?'

He grinned widely. 'Oh, fine past all! I left all my hurts out in the bush this morning. My father wants to make something for you. What would you like?'

'Do you think he would cast me a brass-something if I modelled the form and shaved the brass?'

'He sure would! But Mommio, I will shave the brass and pump the bellows! *The Colas All Fell Face Up!*'

When Suo came out on his porch to take the night-wrappings off Moon Halo, he looked sour. 'I regret,' he said stiffly, 'that it was Comma's belly and not my head that led you to Lega.'

'No mind! I will have need for your head again.'

'Maybe I could use my head to get you along with Bola when she goes to the sacred swamp for clay. I think I will have need for a new pot.'

'Do you sell pots, Suo?'

'I wholesale Bola's pots to Baysah, but this one is for my own self. You see, I put my valuables in a clay pot before I seal them in cement. In case I decide to sell my Tolds for cement, I will need a new pot because the old one will get spoiled beyond all fix in getting it out.'

'Oh? So, you are going to sell me your Tolds?'

'I might,' he said peevishly. 'But you have got to put a handle there.' (Add something to what I had offered.)

'What thing makes a proper handle, Suo?'

'*Salt!*' His voice was crisp with hope.

XII

WHITE MAN ON THE MAT

Pain makes of all people, one tribe.

THE FIRST big market exceeded even Suo's expectations. So many people came from outlying villages there was not enough space in the market compound for all of them to spread their wares. The overflow unfurled mats against the walls of near-by houses. Suo's satisfaction bloated his greedy features into a semblance of goodwill as he moved among them, extracting one cent from each seller, booty to swell Falali's capital.

I watched this through a finger-width opening of the door in my house. I had been instructed to wait until the people were all seated before I made what Zabogi hoped would be the grand entry into the compound.

Johnny and Zabogi had held a mournful consultation over my wardrobe the afternoon previous to the market. According to them, I just didn't have a thing fit to wear for the momentous occasion.

I eavesdropped on their conversation while I was seated in the banana grove just back of my house. There is a gap between the 'collar' on top of mud walls and the framework of poles and rattan which support the thatch. Rats, snakes, and sounds have easy entry and exit through this opening.

'A Kpuesi couldn't go dressed much worse,' Johnny lamented.

There was considerable truth in what he said. My trail clothes were heavy whipcord breeches and khaki shirts. They

had been patched with new cloth in long strips to cover the
gashes which saw-grass had slashed in them on other journeys.
I had brought a few dresses but they were at the tag-end of
two years' wear. Poor Boy, the washman, had thickened the
starch as the fabric thinned. I had not realized how threadbare
they were until I saw them unstarched and unironed, their
present condition. They had been taken off the clothes-line
under our house by the chimpanzees, who delighted in
dragging the laundry through red mud which stains like a
dye. The sun had drained them of colour until what remained
was only a hint of the original hue.

'Haven't you got something fine that she could wear?'
Zabogi asked. 'A shirt or something.'

Johnny thought not. 'She's too plenty awkward-long,
Zabogi. She never fits nothing.'

'Didn't she bring some cloth for *dashes*? Maybe Suo could
run something up quick-like on Moon Halo.'

A pause. Johnny considering. 'There are some fine *lappa*-
lengths, but I don't think she will agree to keep one herself.'

'Don't ask her,' Zabogi advised. 'Just take one, let's take
the brightest, and make it a surprise. You got to manage
women, Johnny. A man can't reason with women.'

'How would we pay Suo? That Suo don't do nothing for
free.'

'We could tell him to skimp on the cut and keep the scraps
for his pay!'

I watched them leave my house walking with the springy
steps of happy conspirators. Johnny had a suspicious bulge
under his uniform in the region of his stomach.

The gaudy *lappa*-lengths I had brought were cotton prints,
seventy inches long, forty-eight inches wide. If Suo took
adequate pay in scraps that dress was going to fit like a sheath.

The only virtue I could attribute to Suo's 'original' was
simplicity. It had a round neck hole, was sleeveless, and the
same size all the way down. I belted it with a raffia cord.

There was a slight fullness at the waist, but in the hips it fitted as tight as a girdle. The only way I could walk in it was to take mincing half-steps. Everyone interested in it, except myself, proclaimed it a sensation.

Both Johnny and Zabogi insisted that the crowd must first see me with my hair down. The afternoon was sultry; all that hair felt like a fur jacket around my shoulders. It seemed highly important to both of them that I made a terrific impression. They had done *their* best with the resources available, so I thought I ought to co-operate.

I leaned against the door-jamb awaiting my cue. The crowd milled around in a great swell of colour. There were several fights between women. I saw Suo beaming at the frays. A few strands of hair pulled, a few dangling breasts twisted like wrung-out garments on wash-day – this kind of thing brings spectators back to the next market, hoping something like it will happen again.

I could not sit down in that dress. Suo's creation did not allow for any posture but one of ramrod erectness. I was weary before Falali finished his welcome address and the market criers had finished proclaiming the price-stabilization rules of the day. All that finished, Zabogi flung open my door and gestured me out with the great flourish of a ringmaster releasing a highly touted lion from a circus cage.

'Shall I show my teeth and growl?' I asked him.

He was too tense about my reception to enjoy this. His grim answer was lost in the roar of the crowd. Only then did he beam his approval. Suo and Johnny joined him as rear-guard. No one bought anything or stirred at all until I had inspected the wares spread on each mat.

There was an abundance of beautiful handmade things as well as heaps of food – eggplants, okra, peanuts, rice, snap beans, tomatoes, tiny onions, garlic, greens of all sorts of strange leaves, pineapples, butter-pears (avocados), mangoes, and oranges, all arranged with an eye for design.

G

Zabogi did the bargaining for what I wanted. He would haggle for fifteen minutes over a penny difference in price, while the crowd strained their ears to catch every detail of the exchange.

'It is fine of you to want to save my money,' I told him, 'but it isn't necessary to work so hard for one penny.'

'I don't care about wasting your money,' he grinned. 'I just don't want people to think I work for a fool!'

'If a person don't have a head, he better let someone else be his head,' Suo said grimly. Much more of this talk, and I would be remembered as The Headless, in spite of my mane of hair.

Johnny collected the booty and we took it back to my house. In my eagerness to get out of that dress and to pile my hair back on top of my head, I forgot I was hobbled. There was a sound of breaking thread and ripping cloth. An attempt at a long stride tripped me into a heap in the dust. Zabogi picked me up and Johnny brushed me off. The crowd howled and pointed.

'What are they saying, Zabogi?'

He listened a minute. 'They are saying, "Look! The white woman wears a dress under a dress! The under one shines and is fine past all! Think of it, two dresses at one time." I'm glad you fell down, Mommio!'

I opened the other seam of the skirt and wore it after that with my black rayon slip filling in the side gaps between the flapping apron-like panels of print in front and rear. Everyone but Suo thought this was an improvement on something already nearly perfect.

I was not able to attend the second big market, the one which featured Tama's beating. I had the double misfortune of malaria and dysentery.

There are other ailments which incur more pain than dysentery, but I know of none more utterly degrading. Bola took complete charge of nursing me through it, and would allow Johnny to do nothing except to attend the 'taboo things' which she did not understand. It was 'taboo' for me to drink water that had not been boiled, or to eat food that had not been cooked in my own utensils, or to take medicine other than the 'white' medicine in my cases. She did persuade him to beat some white clay in a mortar until it was fine as talcum and bake it with cassava starch. I ate a paste of this and I think it is what put me on my feet, together with the atabrin with which Johnny plied me.

'You forget to take the fever medicine every day, didn't you?' he accused me. 'All the time, the Forgets! You sure would have been dead long since if I didn't make yourself my care!'

When Bola could think of nothing else to do for me, she rubbed me from head to foot with sesame oil which she made in my house by pounding the sesame seeds in a mortar and boiling them up in water, after which the clear oil floated to the surface. Zabogi explained that she was pulling strength out of herself and putting it into me. Indeed, it did seem that was the way of it. As I grew stronger, her massive strength seemed to dwindle. Her lustrous skin began to look grey and drawn, her eyes weary. At night, she lay on a mat on the floor, and I could not so much as turn my head on the pillow without her being instantly alarmed and hovering over me.

Lega and Falila came together to see me, with Zabogi to interpret. I had often wondered whether their complicated relationship to each other and to Bola was still a source of friction. Since I had seen Lega doing his own cooking, I assumed that he had not taken another wife after Bola was restored to Falali.

Lega entered the door first, Falali trailing by several paces. Lega stood with his arms crossed, looking down at me. Falali waddled to the far side of the partition at the foot of my bed. At the onset of the malarial delirium, I had kicked a keyhole-shaped opening through the clay-and-wattle wall; my feet protruded through it comfortably to a pad which Bola had arranged for correct height on the far side.

Falali was highly intrigued by the sight of my bare feet. He exclaimed and beckoned to Lega to come and see the rare sight. 'No hoof-stuff grows on the bottom! They are as smooth as a baby's! Does it not hurt to walk on such tender feet? They look new. They are only half a foot wide, but long past all!'

Bola treated both men as though they were little boys who had better mind their manners, or else! She shushed Falali and pushed him down to sit on the floor. Lega sat down without being told. Then she gave them to understand that if anyone talked it would be myself, not them.

Now that I 'had Lega's ear', it seemed it should have been easy to persuade him against the trial, but this was not the case.

'How can you have a trial if no one accuses?' I asked him through Zabogi. 'I refuse to accuse.'

Lega explained that when a person has been accused of anything serious, he must either be convicted or cleared. A spoiled name stays spoiled until it is cleaned. 'Accuses hanging loose in the air are a poison to all the people. A man's good name is the only wealth he has and holds beyond his death; a good name is not wrapped with the corpse and buried.'

I could understand this. I then tried to get him to change the form of the trial, to make it hot-cutlass ordeal. I had already seen a hot-cutlass trial in which no one had been hurt. The blade was heated in a fire until it was glowing. It was then plunged into the earth, quickly withdrawn, and stroked against the bare backs of several suspects. Not one of them cringed. When the diviner approached the final possible culprit, the boy focused his eyes on the point of the cutlass, bellowed with terror, and promptly confessed.

Lega was not to be swayed. He said that the diviner who had been engaged for the ordeal always conducted his trials with hot oil so that was the kind that would be held. Falali nodded 'amens' to everything Lega said. Bola was nervous all through the conversation. Her face was tight with disgust and she 'set her eye hard' on both men. After they left, she swished a damp towel around the room as though to clear the place of smoke.

On the day of Tama's beating, I thought Bola would want to watch her son demonstrate that he could chief a wife, so I suggested that she leave me while she attended the market. She shook her head.

'Tama will have to be beaten many times,' she asked Zabogi to tell me. 'I will watch the next time if I have nothing better to do.' Zabogi shook his head sadly as though he knew it were true and he was tired of the whole business.

Johnny gave me a colourful account of the beating after it was over.

'The busy old clouds above the compound sat down to watch,' he said. 'Now when a cloud sits down to watch, that is a something.'

Tama had rubbed a skin-irritant all over her back. It was a certain leaf which 'itches so plenty, that a beating feels good, like a cold bath'. Zabogi had purchased a new wife-beater especially for the day. It was made of reeds bound in leather which had been stained with camwood. To dye anything with camwood means that the heart-wood of the tree has to be scraped into sawdust before the pigment can be boiled out. 'Wasn't that fine of Zabogi to show such plenty take-care? Some men would have beaten a wife with just any old stick!' But that was not all! The handle of this fine wife-beater was woven with white grass intermixed with black monkey skin. 'Any woman would have been proud to be beaten with that.'

Zabogi had stood directly behind Tama, both of them facing the crowd. He had flexed the wife-beater to show that it was limber, that it would sting rather than bruise. Then, he manfully 'laid on the twenty-five.'

Not once did Tama cry out. The fearful itching set her whole self in a roll, Johnny said, and none could see where the rolling began or stopped. It was like wind blowing through grass without beginning or end. No one had ever before seen anything so like a song, and a dance, and a drum, all rolled into one. The velvet *lappa* took up the roll like waves spreading through water. The women cheered and the men were so done-in they rolled in the dust.

'How did Zabogi look?'

'Well, he looked more chiefly when he began than when he finished. From the way the men acted, I think it will be only small-time until he has to beat Tama again.'

Johnny's voice went into a higher excited treble, a tone he always used when relaying a particularly titillating bit of gossip. 'Who do you think went with her to the waterside to wash the itching powder off her back when it was all over?'

'Not Comma?'

'Yep! That fool, Comma! Always standing under a dead limb. If this one falls, it will crack his empty head wide open.'

'Poor old Zabogi!' I said.

'It's his own fault,' Johnny declared. 'He should never have married that rumpscuttle of a Tama.'

'Where did you get that word, Johnny? Rumpscuttle?'

'From Suo,' Johnny said. 'Suo has got a big book and the name of it is Dictionary. All New Africans got them. Maybe you don't know that book? It is a big fat one all stuffed with lawyer-English. Suo told me that for sixpence he would put more long words in my head. "Rumpscuttle" was a free sample. But I am going to make him knock off one cent because I told him about "bias". Think of that, Mommio. A proper tailor taking bias from me!'

'I'll tell you the one to do, Johnny. Make Suo count it one cent every time you give him a word he doesn't know without the dictionary to help him. He may end up owing you!'

Johnny stared at me for a full minute. 'Why, Mommio! You have got a head after all!' He studied over the possibilities. 'Let's see, hemp, helicon, heddle. . . .'

'You better let me give you the meanings of those,' I said.

'Oh, no mind, seeing you are sick. I'll just make up some meanings, quick-like.' Then he remembered that Suo had the fat book on his side with all its indisputable authority. 'OK,' he sighed. 'I guess you will have to tell me the true meanings. What a bother that Suo can read. I bet I could make up better meanings than the ones they have already got!'

The carriers came in a group to visit me every afternoon while I had to keep to my bed. Bola had her own ideas about visiting hours. Sometimes she kept them waiting outside the house for an hour or more before she would admit them.

When Bola needed words to communicate with me, she called one of her sons. After Tama's shameful conduct during her beating, Bola would not let her come near. I noticed that when Bola wanted to tell some tribal lore, it was Comma, rather than Zabogi, whom she summoned. I think she wanted Comma as well as myself to learn these things.

She had him tell me that in the old days there was a great dispute among the Tellers-of-Tales about which was the greatest chief who ever lived. She said it was one Masabumu, a warrior who led his men to victory by crossing a river on the backs of turtles, who rushed together to form a living bridge. Others said it was Peyulu, the arrow-proof. Had not Peyulu worn around his neck on a thong the vulvae he had cut from a hundred slain women of the enemy tribe? (Woman is considered the source of all life and strength. The custom of taking the life-sources of slain women grew out of the belief that this concentration of life-power passed in strength to the warriors.)

The dispute grew hot because Tellers-of-Tales have the ready use of words to put heat under their thoughts. They finally agreed that they would let the wisest man alive decide the matter. The wisest man was also the oldest because Time thatches the heads of even the stupid with sense.

'The greatest of chiefs was neither of these,' said the old man.

'Who else?' They thought the Old One had left some of his sense in the jungle.

'The greatest of all chiefs is Pain,' said the wise man. 'Those who have carried his weight, even though they have been enemies, are all one tribe. They bear his mark. Pain is the paramount chief who sees over the tribal bounds and is blind to the colour of a man's skin.'

The only ones who laughed were those who had never stood under the hammock-frame of Chief Pain nor felt his dreadful weight upon their heads.

My malaria attack was over soon. I have all but forgotten the horrors of that illness in Boitai, but I never smell the rich, cereal odour of sesame seed without rekindling my gratitude for the mother-shine of that black woman who spent her strength to make me well.

G*

XIII

COALS OF FIRE KINDLED

*The hand does not fear what the heart has
not darkened.*

IT CAME at last, the day of the trial I was unable to prevent. I was awake early after sleeping badly. Even though
Lega seemed to have accepted Comma as a son, an appren-
tice, and a spiritual heir (this was implied in the apprentice-
ship), I was uneasy. I had dreamed that the pot of boiling
oil tipped over, running into the depressed area of the market
compound like molten lava, forming a steaming tarry lake
from which the trapped multitude screamed for help. Demons
in the sky, wearing the masks of the Poro, peeked from
behind the edges of ominous clouds and roared with fiendish
glee. Their terrible laughter shook the clouds into a semblance
of sagging mirth-wobbled bellies of overweight monsters
gorged on the miseries which man invents for his torture.

After that dream there was no use trying to sleep. I dressed and faced the perplexities of packing for the trip back to the coast.

We were to leave Boitai early the following day. The carriers wanted to stay longer. So did I, but it was uncertain just when there would be a place for me on a plane back to the United States so I dared not linger up-country. When Zabogi had carried me into Boitai, he had shouted that he was taking me home. That is exactly the way I felt about Boitai and its people. I should have liked to stay for a long time.

It had been my plan to take back to the coast only the bare essentials. I had judged that at least six cases, emptied of food and *dashes*, could be left behind for a final *dash* to the chief. A box with a hinged lid is a treasure in a village where every board has to be hand-sawed from a tree trunk, every nail separately and patiently fashioned by the black-smith. Hinges start by trapping a live animal to get the skin which becomes the leather from which doors are swung and lids are attached to cases.

I stared at the heap of things I had been *dashed* and had added to by purchase. I doubted whether these could all be crammed in the cases if I used every one. All my life I have been amazed at intervals by the mountain of things I seem to amass, every one treasured, but impossible of storage and transport. I leave them someplace, move on to another, and if I manage to get back to them again the surprise and delight of discovering them the second time is as keen as when I acquired them in the first place.

Now, I had really overburdened myself, but I had not the heart to discard a single item. The men would have to make *kinjas* for the overflow and I would need extra carriers. This, I knew, would have to be fully arranged before the trial. No one would give a thought to anything but that from noon until sundown when we were to have our farewelling. Zabogi wanted us to leave Boitai in the dark before the next dawn, to slip quietly and unwept. There would be tears spilt enough, he said, at the evening event, and who can face his mother's tears in the early morning when even the cheeks of the sun are streaming? The men would not have it in them to leave if they had to say a double set of goodbyes.

I was still tottery on my feet from the illness and trembly now from remembered fragments of the dreams which insisted themselves between my eyes and that enormous pile of miscellany I had to sort. When packing a head load, one has to consider not only how one object fits against another, but the total weight in each carton, and the distribution of heavy things throughout, so the crate will balance on a man's head without aid from his hands.

Johnny came in when the struggle began to seem ill matched to my strength. He shoved coffee under my nose.

'I heard you rattling around in here,' he scolded. 'I never told you it was time for you to get up.'

'All those *things* told me, Johnny. I think the men will have to spend the morning making carrying-*kinjas*.'

'Oh, no!' He appeared devastated by the news.

'Oh, yes!' I saw I was going to have to be firm, perhaps even 'throw a vex'.

'Things! Things are what humbug the life out of white people! Always a big palaver for plenty things,' he grumbled. 'If twenty *pickin* get borned out of you, you got enough elephant-hoof bracelets to ring the arms of all from wrist to shoulder. If you get to be head-wife over a hundred women, you got enough belled anklets to keep track of where every one of the hundred goes by the sound of the bells. If you never see another market, you got enough country-cloth to wrap you forever.'

'But I want them all. So, tell Zabogi to set the men to making *kinjas* and bargain for more carriers.'

He sighed. 'But Ma, you will *spoil our day!* We were going to make play!'

'You can make play when we get back to the plantation. This morning, we make *kinjas.*'

'We cannot make this play at the plantation, not any day but today. We were going to give Old Shake to the people of Boitai! We got little boxes all made and keys for them, and palm kernels cut for rings, and Dika is going to wear a head-cloth and one of your dresses and be Portia, and we are going to let Suo be Shylock because he understands interest – and now we got to make *kinjas* because you don't know when too much is enough!'

'Well, it doesn't take very long to make *kinjas.* Let's get busy and pack this up so we can see how many we will need.'

He set to work but not with hearty goodwill. His mind was not on the packing. The men were not going to like those loads!

'Ma, who did Shakespeare shake his spear at?'

'No one,' I said absently, rearranging some ill-mated objects he had dumped together. 'That's just the name he had. Now let's start out by putting one heavy thing in the bottom of each box.'

'No name is *just* a name,' he said irritably. 'Names mean more than anything. When Suo riddled me that, I didn't know the answer. Come on now, Ma, hang head on it and give me a proper reason.'

'Well, what does Johnny mean, for instance? It's just a name. That box is going to be too heavy.'

'Johnny is not just a name. It means to take everything I bother to pay mind to, and swell it up big, so everyone will look and laugh.'

'Right now, Johnny better mean to pay mind to packing!'

He didn't even glance at what his hands were doing.

'When I asked you what your name meant, you told me about that wicked old Haman so I knew that "Esther" means to stand behind people and help them. Now, you refuse to help me answer Suo.'

Johnny never allowed anyone to half-listen to him. He demanded and eventually got the listeners' 'full ear'. When the truth didn't satisfy him, one had to invent an answer that would; he continued to pester until he got something he considered worth retelling. I might just as well stop and think up something to put upon the bard of Avon, if I wanted to get the packing finished.

'Well, I guess you might say that his pen was his spear. When he shook it at people, all their secrets came rattling out. Then he quick-like caught the secrets on paper so we can know why they acted the way they did.'

'Old Shake should have shook harder! I don't know why Tonio made a loan for only three moons. With our people, sometimes it is the son of a man's son that is caught by an old debt-palaver. Sometimes the boy don't even know what his grandfather bought with the money, or even that he owed it, but he has got to pay it all the same. I am going to change that three moons business to three rice plantings. No one would believe it else.'

Johnny had dumped a brass anklet which weighed at least five pounds on a fragile little clay dye-pot.

'Look at what you've done! That was one of Bola's best pieces!'

'I think you read it wrong, Ma. I think it must say three rice plantings.'

'Just let me pack the clay pots, will you, Johnny? I can't look it up because I left Old Shake back at the plantation.'

'Better you should have brought him and left off carrying clay pots,' he said without a trace of remorse. 'Well, there's one we won't have to carry. They sure fit in the box better when they're broke!'

'Is Comma in your play?' I was wondering whether Comma was finally feeling apprehension about the ordeal, whether he was awakening to the day of the trial in a shiver of fear.

'Sure,' Johnny said. 'I let him be old Bassani because he has finally learned to reach for the right thing.'

'If you don't watch what you are doing, I am going to reach for Comma to do this packing,' I threatened him. That brought him around to a little more care.

'I only broke three pots and one spoon,' he defended his record. 'So far.'

I did not expect to be entertained by their production. I attended for the sole purpose of observing Comma's behaviour. It was a holiday in the village, even Lega sat with the others in the compound. He beckoned me to come and sit beside him and he shook his head wonderingly as he saw me tensely clasping and unclasping my hands as we waited for the flurried actors to bustle through their last-minute preparations in front of the hut which was their backdrop. There was a large stack of wood on the edge of the compound which had not been there before. For the ordeal fire? I had imagined that this would be a small fire, possibly the size of a cooking fire. There was enough wood stacked there for the whole village to use during a couple of evenings. I pointed to it. Lega nodded and smiled. He was certainly not doing any worrying.

The audience was brought to attention by a blast on a *gbonga* horn. Dika, with one of my dresses trailing limply around his ankles, brought out three caskets and explained their import. They were three hunks of wood, one in the natural state (iron, since they are not familiar with lead) one rubbed with white clay (silver), and one wrapped in yellow cloth (gold). A key, suspended by a thong, hung from each. The 'gold' one was secured by a Commodore Hotel key, still bright and new-looking. The language, pidgin turned

into Loma by Zabogi after each speech, was far from Eliza-
bethan, but it had a surprising flair for the humour and the
essence of the tale. There was vehement audience-participation
in the problem of making a wise choice among the caskets.
It seemed for a while that the spectators might actually wrest
the play from the actors. This is exactly the kind of problem
they will spend hour after hour discussing in all its ramifica-
tions. They probably still argue sometimes in Boitai whether
Portia's 'photo' was in the proper box.

Suo, as Shylock, came to court with an enormous cutlass
which he whetted on a rock most of the time he was not
speaking. He tested the cutting edge on a dry banana leaf,
glinted sunlight off the bright surface, and prodded 'Tonio'
with the handle to find the most succulent spot for slicing.
Comma went through his role effortlessly and seemed to be
having as good a time as the others. As 'Bassani' begged to
assume the ordeal for his friend, he seemed entirely unmindful that his own ordeal, which was not make-believe,
was no more than an hour away.

I watched Lega as the entertainment progressed. This was
the first time I had seen him appear completely relaxed.
When he laughed it was inwardly and silently, showing only
in little crinkles that gathered at the corners of his eyes and
in parted lips, but the remarkable thing was that he laughed
at all. I was now able to stretch imagination to picture him
seated around a mat with Falali and other men on that long-
ago day, throwing the cowries, which, because they fell in
his favour, were responsible for all that was happening in
the present. Before this, I simply could not see Lega involved
in anything so trivial as throwing the shells. My own presence in Boitai at the moment had hinged on the chance fall
or 'four face up' as those shells rolled over the mat sixteen
years before. If all the 'if's' were deleted from life. . . .

The crowd went into an uproar of rejoicing when Dika
made the point (so understandable to a tribesman) that not

one drop of blood might be drawn. There was no curtain to drop so Zabogi simply nodded at the crowd and announced, 'Make-play finished.' The audience took it from there, took it home with them to their huts in excited chatter and delighted laughter. I feel sure that on many cool rainy nights when the only sounds are the dripping of water from the eaves and the sputter of the fire in the centre of the floor, they have brought Old Shake down out of the thatch and polished him up with rememberings. It struck me as I watched, that his plays may have had somewhat the same zest in the beginning before they became a cult for scholars or a bore to sophomores. The first audiences undoubtedly wore more clothes, but perhaps they, too, were ordinary excitable people willing to be put under the spell of a good story, and there must have been some among them who could not read.

People from the surrounding villages started drifting into the compound before the play was finished. If the afternoon had not offered the high excitement of a trial by ordeal, the actors would certainly have had to do a repeat performance for the market crowd.

Johnny and Zabogi both urged me to chew cola nuts to 'grow strength for a long day'. I had in mind that as a last resort on the trek home, I might eat cola 'to put iron in the legs', but I wanted all my powers of observation accurate and clear for the trial. Many speculations have been made on the part which hypnosis may play in the apparent outcome of ordeals. I wanted no fuzzy impressions of what I would see and hear.

I was too excited to want any lunch so I sat in the shade of the overhang of my house and drank tea. I could look across the compound to Lega's house. Squatted in front of it, father and son were boiling up a midday snack. From that distance, they seemed of one age. Lega was as supple and had the same tardive grace about his movements as

Comma. At intervals, I saw the white flash of their teeth as they spoke or smiled. One might think they had nothing more on their minds for the afternoon ahead than a comradely excursion into the jungle to set snares for game.

The sasswood-player (diviner) was an ancient from a nearby village, famous for his occult power. He was tardy for the trial, a cause of grave concern for the expectant throng. Late-comers, trailing in with their wares, noisily demanded space to spread their produce, causing confusion and shifting in the market area. Suo circulated among them continuously, demanding to see 'receipts' for the pennies that had been paid. This was the first of the hundreds of markets I had attended where receipts were part of the ritual. These were little slivers of bamboo marked with red lead. Anyone could duplicate the slivers but Suo had what was probably the only can of lead paint between Boitai and the plantation.

Falali did the honours during the wait by ladling out generous servings of palm wine from great pots on the piazza of his house. Every time he offered a gourdful to a guest, he took a sizable gulp himself to demonstrate that it was free from poison and 'witch'. The more he drank, the wider he smiled. After he became too intoxicated to trust his weight above his feet, he summoned Bola to do the serving and sampling. She only pretended to sip. I saw that her hand trembled and that some of the yeasty fermented palm sap sloshed over on the floor. Bola, at least, did not feel confident about the way the afternoon would end.

The diviner hobbled into town at last, his gnarled hands clasped over a knobby walking-stick. The stick, having been polished all along its length by much handling, seemed with its gloss and its grain to be a more living thing than the dependant it held erect. The crowd hushed reverently as he made his way through. '*Keke!*' they murmured. '*Aye, Keke!*' The word means 'uncle' but it is also a title of great respect.

Keke was winterish-looking and wizened, his skin all

wrinkled and leathery folds like a black walnut that has hung overlong on a tree and which surely cannot persist against many more gusts of wind. His eyes were milky and staring. They seemed not so much sightless as seeing through the present to dim reaches which might be either the remembered past or the soon-to-be-expected future with the Old Ones who had already fallen. He gave the impression of looking through and beyond you in the way that very old people do when they call you by your mother's name instead of your own because they knew her when she was your present age.

Zabogi introduced me to Keke, and when he took my hand into his, it was like being clasped by a kindly claw that didn't quite know what to do with the curious object it had accidently fastened on to.

'His spirit is already with the Old Ones who are gone,' Zabogi said. 'He is not blind but he can't see you. So, never mind that he doesn't say his *Boi Avas* [friendly greetings]. He has become *dulu* [a little child] with age.'

I didn't mind the lack of amenities. What I did mind was that the chief, who was supposed to preside, was so drunk that everything seemed wondrously gay to him, and that the diviner was so senile that everything present was apparently vague.

Keke huddled and shivered in his skimpy robe in spite of the humid heat. He would allow no one to assist him in the smallest detail of preparing for the trial. He had a skin pouch slung over his shoulder, his *baka* which contained his medicine-magic. He took this off and hung it under the eaves of the house nearest the pile of wood. The one thing of which he was acutely aware was this *baka*. If anyone passed within feet of it, he berated, threatened, and almost collapsed with concern. This was the tangible source of his power, his link with the supernatural, and it must not be contaminated by anyone's touch.

I have no way of knowing what was inside the *baka*. There had been quite a flurry at one time on the plantation when a rash of these *bakas* appeared in the labour camps. The workers from other tribes said that the Lomas were 'making strong medicine for bad' and threatened to leave work unless the medicine bags were all confiscated, after which they quietly disappeared. I was able to obtain one of them through devious means. The owner didn't want it any longer; the medicine in it had 'gone dead', but he had to be very sly about selling it to me so that his Loma friends would not find out. The Bassaus who were the most terrified at this time whispered that 'there is always a human heart wrapped up in a *baka*'. Inside the one we have, there is something a little smaller than my fist wrapped up in stained country-cloth, but I have never been able to bring myself to unwrap it.

Keke would allow no one to touch the wood for the fire. He built it up bigger and bigger, crouched so close to it that I thought his swishing robe would surely catch from the sparks. Although perspiration rolled into the crevices of his seamed face, he continued to shiver.

'The spirits are gathering inside him,' Zabogi told me. 'That is why he is so cold and full of shakes.'

No one had thought to explain to me that the wood had to be 'cleaned' by fire before it could be used in the trial. I saw that after a log was burned on the outside, Keke transferred the solid core of remains to a separate pile. From this fire-cleansed wood, he selected certain sticks for a third fire which he placed on the ordeal spot. The crowd was not the least restless during this drawn-out proceeding; they sat hushed and tense.

Finally, he had everything just the way he wanted it, the fire properly placed and hot, a three-legged iron ring over it to support an enormous clay pot (not yet in place), the supply of rich red palm oil to be heated, the polished brass belled anklet which Comma was to pluck from the bottom of the pot, and a kettle full of leaves which he had bruised in a mortar until they were an arsenic-green paste. Besides these things, there was one other clay pot containing what appeared to be water.

It was time then to get Falali on the scene. This took some doing. He was in a stupor from heat and wine, still smiling like an overweight sleeping cherub. Four men eventually half carried, half dragged him into place in front of the hut from which Keke's *baka* hung. He kept lolling off his chief-chair, and since they had to keep him on it somehow, Bola finally propped him up by placing two of the younger wives on each side of him. They batted his swaying weight back and forth between them.

Keke now placed the ordeal pot in the iron stand over the fire and poured the palm oil into it. I watched to see the shade of colour of the oil. It has been said that the oil may be only a film on top of water in these trials and that the water would not be as damaging to living tissues as oil. As far as I could see, the oil was as rich a red-brown as palm oil ever is.

Keke made a long oration while the oil was heating.

'He is telling what an evil thing it is to steal,' Zabogi explained to me. Zabogi and Bola and I were sitting as close to the fire as Keke would allow. 'He is telling the people the names of different-different Lomas who stole.'

From the length of the harangue, I thought he must be enumerating the tribe from the first man through 'all his begats'.

'Now, he is telling what was done to them,' Zabogi said. 'If any Loma does a bad thing, it is the man's own family who have to do the punishment. That punishes them for letting one of themselves go bad.'

'The burns aren't punishment enough?'

'Oh, no,' Zabogi said. 'The burns are the smallest part of it.'

Keke had the crowd completely under his spell. Some of the women began to sob.

'They remember now the terrible day they had to help punish someone in their own family,' Zabogi said.

I hoped Zabogi would not feel it necessary to describe these punishments in detail. Before the trial I had told him over and over that he must translate *everything* that was said and done, so now it was too late to spare myself the grisly history Keke was repeating in order to admonish all the spectators to the upright life. Some of the offenders had been hacked to pieces with cutlasses, some of them had been laid in leaf-lined *kinjas* and covered on all sides with pounded hot-pepper pods, some had been tied in line of march of driver ants, some had been flogged with firebrands. 'So it is done to those who break the law of the Lomas.'

Slate-blue smoke was pouring off the heated oil by the time Keke finished his exhortations. Most of the crowd was moaning and swaying in a rhythm of misery. I was trembling and drenched with perspiration. Bola had her strong arm around me, whether to comfort me or to herself receive comfort, I don't know. Keke then sent Zabogi to fetch Comma. He came out of the house with Lega, both of them walking erect with long, brisk strides. Lega sat down beside Zabogi, Comma took his place behind the smoking pot.

Keke then talked to the pot, told it that if Comma had not stolen, it must not hurt him in the least, but that if he had spoiled the Loma name along with his own, it must bite him deep. Comma looked at his mother and me. Bola looked steadily back at him, steeling him with her own strength.

Keke next addressed Comma, telling him that he could refuse the trial, confess without the ordeal if he wished and take the punishment the Old Ones would decide. Comma shook his head, indicated that the trial should go on. Lega nodded proud approval. Keke next took the paste of leaves and smeared it in a thick coating over Comma's right hand and arm, being careful to get it between all the fingers. Then he held up the three-knobbed brass ring and spoke at length about it. The paste of leaves was meanwhile drying into a crust over Comma's hand. It had turned a shade of sage-green where it was thinnest. There was less smoke coming off the oil now and it was less blue in colour. After another coating of the paste was rubbed on Comma, the brass anklet was dropped into the pot. Quick as a flash, Comma dived his hand in after it and brought it up, dripping oil as red as blood. A great collective sigh swept like wind through the crowd and then the roar of approval and triumph. They carried him off to the waterside on their shoulders. Keke was completely ignored now, and when they almost brushed his *baka* in the surge, he prated un-attended. Bola crushed me to her and we wept unashamedly on each other's shoulders. After all the tense waiting, the imagined horror, it was over and done with in a moment and had come out all right!

I ask no one to believe one thing or another about trials by ordeal. All I can do is to tell what I saw, and leave it at that. Those who are not able to accept the unlikely will probably find the explanation in whatever insulation there was in the paste of leaves.

Suo plucked at my sleeve. 'Time to dig up the Tolds!'

Zabogi went along with Suo and me, armed with some formidable weapons to crack the concrete 'safe' under Suo's floor.

About three feet of iron pipe led down diagonally under the packed-earth floor to the concrete-encased pot. The top end of the pipe, which protruded six inches or so above the floor, was plugged with a wad of raffia. All Suo needed to do to add to the underground treasure was to unstopper the pipe and drop in the coins. Once inside this 'piggy-bank' there was no way to get them out except to excavate the pot at the lower end of the pipe and break it out of the concrete. Zabogi did the labour, Suo the grunting.

'I thought it must be almost full, and I would soon have to have a bigger pot,' Suo said. 'Else, I would not have sold the Tolds so cheap.'

In the bottom of the pot was the proof I wanted. Suo had written out a bill of sale for one male chimpanzee, sold for the sum of fifty dollars, American money, to Comma, son of Bola, and the date. Comma had signed the paper with the familiar flourish, a big C in which the other letters of his name were nested, and under it for good measure, he had made a neat row of commas. The bill of sale enclosed another paper, the bill from the Firestone Trading Company for which Suo had reproved me. These were wrapped around fifty dollars in United States bills and coins.

'Well, that's that!' Suo said. 'Palaver finished.'

'Not quite finished,' I said. 'I still don't know what happened to the chimpanzee. I never have believed that Comma was robbed, though he most certainly was beaten.'

'Ask him,' Suo suggested. 'He will tell you the truth now that you are ready to swallow it.'

Suo was anxious to get Comma away from the market crowd. Unsold produce would cripple the next market. Comma, back from the waterside now, was still the centre of attention.

'Walk to the pond of sacred fish,' Suo said. 'I will send Comma there.'

The pool was stocked with enormous tame catfish. No one had ever been allowed to catch them and they were fed every morning with the excrement of the most respected elders of the town so that generation after generation, their body-stuff might be built from and incorporate the body-stuff of the Old Ones. The jungle came up to the edge of the pond and was hung with a curtain of flowering vines. Prominent among them was the exotic *strophanthus* with blossoms the rich and fragile pink-purple of a Negro palm. The Lomas saw in the tube-flowers and buds phallic symbols, powerful medicine, and arrow poison. (Later, researchers from a prominent drug firm saw in them an early precursor of the drug cortisone.)

The place seemed ancient and sombre in spite of the cascade of flowers. Here and there, a nooselike bend of a liana hung below the crown of the forest as though it had started earthward and then been drawn upward again by the power of the sun. I was sleepy now that the long-sustained excitement was relieved. Bees buzzed in the pollen and I drowsed.

A brown seed-pod as large as a melon fell to the earth and burst with a punky thud at my feet. When I opened my eyes to see what had made the sound, Comma was standing above me, smiling down at me.

'Go on and sleep if you like, Mommio,' he said. 'I will stand guard.'

'Suo said you would tell me the truth about the chimpanzee, Comma. Will you?'

'For true, I will,' he said. 'First, I must show you my back.'

He peeled out of his shirt, and there, running from the nape of his neck to his waist, were parallel rows of scars, entirely healed but still pink and newish-looking, the tooth-marks of the Poro Devil!

'I agreed for the Devil to swallow me when I came to Lomaland to buy the chimpanzee,' he said. 'I knew then that I could never be anything unless I first tried small-small to become part of my people. The making of the marks is only the first part of the Poro, but it is something. Suo told me that he would arrange for the chimpanzee while I was in the bush, and this he did. I took it from him and signed the bill and started out in the night.'

'But why? Why did you have to leave in the night?'

'It was whispered around that the Poro had need of a chimpanzee for sacrifice. I wanted to get gone with that one before it was asked of me. *No man can refuse what the Poro asks.'*

'And did you leave without any knowing?'

'I didn't manage it,' he said. 'The Devil's messenger over-took me on the path and asked for the chimp so I had to give it to him; there was nothing else I could do.'

'Did you struggle with him? Was it he that beat you?'

'Oh, no, no struggle. I just gave it to him. *If he had asked me to kill you, then I would have had either to kill myself to keep from killing you or else I would have had to do the one he asked.'*

'Which would you have done, in that case, do you think?'

'Well,' he said, 'I don't think I could want to live after I had murdered someone so I suppose I would have killed myself first and not after. But, then, who can say the one he will do?'

'How did you get beaten then?'

'Well, all the way back to the plantation I hung head to think what I could tell you. I didn't think you could swallow the truth; that is why I tailored a lie. The truth is, after I sweat out a lie to tell, I beat myself up so you would believe it.' (What a thorough job he had made of it!)

'Where did you get the money to redeem Bola?'

He looked at me wide-eyed. 'Why, I saved it! Don't you remember that I always gave almost all my pay back to you to send down to the bank in Monrovia? If you have forgotten that, you can ask them to see the records. I held out only a little for rice money and I even saved most of that.'

He had earned about fifty dollars a year and had needed only about four cents a day to live on. This added up.

'Is it stealing to take food from animals, Ma?'

'I suppose not,' I said 'Not if you leave them enough.'

'Well, that's all I ever stole, just animal rice. Every Monday when you would measure out the rice for the week for the chickens and the monkeys and the chimpanzees and the antelope and the dogs and the cat, and put the stalk of bananas in my charge, I would take a little pinch from the portion of each animal and live on it myself. That way, I could save even my rice money to buy my mother free. But I never stole any other thing from you.'

'You were already marked by the Poro, Comma. Why then, did you dread to enter Boitai with me?'

'Oh, the marks on the back are the least thing, the first of many degrees,' he said. 'Lega wanted me to go ahead with the rest, to work my way up. I told him I wanted to work my way up into *white* learning. There was cold between us over that when I had last seen him.'

When boys first enter the Poro, they know the Big Devil only by his voice which they hear in spine-tingling noises coming off the hills at night. He is thought to be Spirit. Not until they have completed a protracted cult course, is he revealed to them as a man, one they have always known. Just what they think when they discover their god become human, walking among them, whether this is a shock or whether they have been prepared during their training to accept it, is something I have not been able to find out. I did not dare ask Comma whether it was something he knew, but he must have suspected it, entering the Poro, as he did, years after his own age group had been initiated.

'Well, what do you think now, Comma? Is it worth it, to give up your white learning to get yourself a father and a tribe? What do you want to make of your life?'

He did not hesitate. 'I want to stay in Boitai and be my father's son. I want to wife Tama and have plenty of children. When they are of the proper age, I want them to get white learning. When that time comes, a boy won't have to decide for one or the other, white ways or tribe ways. Zabogi will be chief and I will be the blacksmith, and we will know what our fathers do not know, that a Loma can be both.'

'Have you talked with your father about wanting Tama?'

'That I have,' he said. 'And he thinks it might be arranged. You know, most tribe people think of wives the way Suo

thinks of a sale – it is a business deal. But my father understands heart-hunger. He has never taken another woman after
my mother went back to Falali. That gives him to understand
the way I feel toward Tama.'

'But how will Zabogi feel about it? And Falali? And your
mother?'

Suo will advise Falali to make a good deal. Tama has had
children already so they will ask a high dowry. Zabogi is a
little tired of having to watch Tama all the time, he has already
told me he would rather have her sister, who is not sassy.
My mother is vexed at Tama but she will come over that in
time. So you see, it could work out the right way for all.'

After our evening meal, we all gathered in the compound
for the third time that day. There was a lengthy exchange of
speeches, gifts, compliments, and well-wishings.

'We want one more thing from you, Ma,' Zabogi said after
the salt, the final *dash*, was in their hands.

'What thing is that?'

'We want that after you get back to your country, you
should "give us to your people," just as you gave your people
to all we.'

Well, here it is, Zabogi. For true, dear friend, I have tried
all my best.